Humpbacks
Unveiling the Mysteries

HUMPBACKS

MAMMALS Like us

SUMMER FEEDERS

Migrations

WINTER BREEDERS

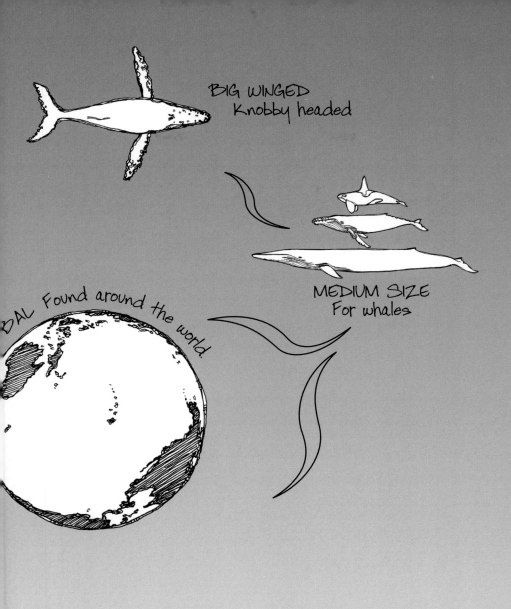

BIG WINGED
Knobby headed

MEDIUM SIZE
For whales

BAL Found around the world.

RECOVERING
From whaling.

Humpbacks
Unveiling the Mysteries

Jim Darling

Photographs by **Flip Nicklin**

Illustrations by **Susan W. Barnes**

GRANVILLE ISLAND PUBLISHING

Library and Archives Canada Cataloguing in Publication

Darling, James David, 1950–
   Humpbacks : unveiling the mysteries / Jim Darling.

Includes bibliographical references and index.
ISBN 978-1-894694-72-8

   1. Humpback whale. 2. Humpback whale--Hawaii. I. Title.

QL737.C424D375 2009   599.5'25   C2009-900152-7

Editors: Graham Hayman and Christine Laurin
Indexer: Bookmarks
Photos: Flip Nicklin (except where otherwise credited)
Illustrator: Susan Wallace Barnes
Graphics: Josie Cleland
Photo preparation and design concepts: Gary Wilcox
Cover designer: Joan Selix Berman

Granville Island Publishing Ltd.
212-1656 Duranleau St · Granville Island
Vancouver BC · Canada · V6H 3S4
info@granvilleislandpublishing.com
www.granvilleislandpublishing.com

First published March 2009
Printed in China

*   *   *

Photographs taken under the authority of National Marine Fisheries Service (NMFS) scientific research permits:

   Permit 987 & 753-1599 (Flip Nicklin, Jim Darling, Meagan Jones, Bill Scott)
   Permit 313-1772 01 (Mark Ferrari)
   Permit 932-1489 (Ed Lyman)

Contents

Acknowledgements

I gratefully acknowledge the key role played by Bob and Pat Steinhoff, who offered inspiration and support for this project during a cruise in Alaska. Their commitment during its development is much appreciated. Sadly, Pat has since passed away and this book memorializes her love of the ocean and the creatures in it.

Whale Trust provided critical, continuing support for this book, which has taken several years to complete. Special thanks to Meagan Jones, who administered the project and also reviewed it and contributed to its content, Bill Scott, who kept things organized financially, and Allen Jones, who advised on marketing.

Whale Trust is extremely grateful to Makana Aloha Foundation for providing a significant portion of the funds for this book.

Flip Nicklin's photographs and Susan Wallace Barnes's illustrations enhance this book tremendously. The donation of their work is typical of their generous support for whale research and education. Many of Flip's photographs were provided through his agency, Minden Pictures, and special thanks are due to Larry Minden and Chris Carey. *National Geographic* magazine graciously allowed the use of several photographs from past articles on humpback whales.

This book is partially based on a technical report, *Characterization of Humpback Whale Behavior in Hawaii*, completed for the Hawaiian Islands Humpback Whale National Marine Sanctuary (HIHWNMS) in 1999 by the author. Thanks are due to Jeff Walters (HIHWNMS co-coordinator) for his role in the initial report.

Additional photographs were contributed by Meagan Jones and Bill Scott (both from Whale Trust), Mark Ferrari (Center For Whale Studies), Ed Lyman (HIHWNMS and NOAA Fisheries Marine Mammal Health and Stranding Program), John Ford on behalf of the late Gordon Pike (Fisheries and Oceans Canada), Koji Nakamura (Japan Underwater Films), Jason A. Moore, Ed Lane, Greg Silber and Fran Gealer. Thank you.

General support for the author (allowing me time to write) came from Sarah Crandall Haney (Canadian Whale Institute) and Gregory Colbert (Flying Elephants Foundation), and is enormously appreciated.

I would also like to take this opportunity to thank the Maui residents who have helped us on many different fronts, for years (decades, actually), including Ron and Diane Roos, Jim Luckey, Tad and Cindy Luckey, Mark and Jeri Robinson, Barry and Irene McPhee, Connie Sutherland and the late Chuck Sutherland. In addition, I thank the many volunteers who have assisted us in the field over the years (please see www.whaletrust.org for names). Most particularly, special thanks are due Karen Miller and Jason Sturgis.

As always, the key to this and all Whale Trust projects is the donors. Their support is greatly appreciated. Space constraints prevent us from naming everyone (please see website), however, a special acknowledgement is due Darlene and Jeff Anderson, Flip Nicklin, Garry Weber, Allen and Ann Jones, Pat and Karyn Cochran, Margaret Sears, Bill Scott, and Mary Whitney and Betsy Collins (Fluke Foundation).

I wish to acknowledge the Granville Island Publishing team in Vancouver (BC), including Jo Blackmore, Graham Hayman, Christine Laurin, Gary Wilcox, François Trahan, Elspeth Richmond, Neall Calvert and Rachel Moffat. Josie Cleland of Lightwave Image Services in Nanaimo (BC) produced the book's graphics and Joan Selix Berman in Maui designed the cover.

As with any project like this, the innocent victims of the author's preoccupation are family and friends. I thank them for their patience and support.

Finally, this book could not have been written without the collective work of dedicated researchers in Hawaii over the last thirty years. I acknowledge their endeavors and hope I have done them justice.

Foreword

For over thirty years now, researchers from around the world have come to study whales in Hawaii. This book is about what we have learned . . . and not learned. It is meant for both novice and experienced whale watchers. For the former, it provides humpback whale basics, answers some questions (or perhaps explains why we can't answer them yet), and hopefully encourages your interest. For the experienced whale watcher (and there are many), this book lets you in on what researchers are doing and thinking. It presents some of the puzzles, challenges, and current hypotheses about whale behavior seen every day through the winter. In either case, whether you're a beginner or a veteran, the intention is for this book to deepen your knowledge about these remarkable creatures with which we share Hawaiian waters.

Humpback whale studies conducted in Hawaii are the basis of this book, with information extracted from over fifty references from the 1970s to the present. In addition, information from selected studies from other regions (many of which have addressed similar or related research questions and add to the discussion of humpback behavior) has been included. Where all the studies relevant to a topic agree, summary statements are made. Where differences in interpretations and alternative ideas have arisen, the arguments for them are introduced and questions that remain open noted. All of the references that provide further information or discussion on the topic are included in the Sources section at the end of the volume.

The information in this book comes from published scientific journals, graduate (MS and PhD) dissertations, technical reports, and several personal communications from researchers. It does not include unpublished field notes or manuscripts in the publication pipeline, all likely to provide exciting new information. Our intention is to reprint this book periodically with the latest updates.

This book is a little different from most. The goal has been to stay very true to what the studies have told us, but also to include some of the research process — the multiple ideas or hypotheses (some eventually proven, many ultimately discarded), as well as the compelling questions that push research forward.

For the non-scientist, it can be frustrating at times when you expect short, simple, black-and-white answers to what seem like basic questions about whales (e.g. Why do they sing? or Why do they breach?). Most researchers have had the experience of a TV documentary director trying desperately to get a concise reply to a question that does not yet have one, although often an 'answer' gets provided to the audience in the editing room! This book doesn't do that, and the hope is you will find it more interesting because of it.

Jim Darling

Chapter 1

Whales!

WHALES! If you have been to Maui (or to any of the Hawaiian Islands) in winter, odds are you have seen humpback whales. In fact, between Christmas and Easter, it's hard to look out to sea and *not* see whales. This is their winter home. Sometimes it takes a few minutes of searching to spot quiet, lone or paired adults offering only puffy blows and a brief glimpse of a back or tail. Other times, splashes from slapping flukes or flippers, the explosions of breaches, or groups of a dozen or so whales racing around in tight formation will grab anyone's attention from miles away.

Everyone sees them, from commuters making the daily trek along the coast, to kids playing on the beach, vacationers lounging on their lanai, waiters moving from bar to table, or local business folks sipping iced tea in one of the waterfront restaurants. They stop what they are doing for a moment (or an hour) to watch, and then continue on with their day. Even if you don't glance out to sea once in a while and are completely unaware of the whales, chances are you will still get caught in Hawaii's unique whale jams, with hundreds of cars pulling to the side of the road (often wildly) to gaze at nearshore action. Hawaii's whales are world-class spectacular and more — they are part of the background, the ambience of the islands.

What Are They Doing Out There?

Humpbacks in Hawaii, both male and female, are trying to pass their genes on to the next generation, if necessary depriving their neighbors of the same opportunity! Virtually all of the behavior we see and hear is part of this ultimate objective. It's critical, complex, and fascinating.

From our knowledge to date, humpback whales appear to be typical mammals in this regard. Individual males go for quantity — that is, to sire as many offspring as possible (preferably all of them). Females, on the other hand, are presumably more interested in quality — finding

During winter it is hard to miss the whales cavorting off Hawaii's shorelines — there are thousands of them.

the most fit male to be the father. There is conflict and resolution within, and between, the sexes.

Hawaii's waters, therefore, swirl with complex social behavior. The whales follow strategies, interact, and form relationships. Individual whales may search, attract, avoid, compete, and cooperate, always weighing off energy cost versus reproductive gain. This drama is on display whenever the whales are in Hawaii, for in the midst of all this they jump and roll and splash and race . . .

The 1970s

Biologists knew very little about 'Hawaiian' humpback whales at the beginning of the 1970s. At the outset, we did not know where these whales came from, where they went, how many were out there, when they were present, and not a single word had been written describing behavior patterns that are popular lore today. In fact, prior to the 1970s, there was little general awareness (public or scientific) that the whales were even in Hawaii!

Whaling of humpback whales had ceased in the northeast Pacific a few years earlier, in 1966. It's not known why, but humpbacks were not actually hunted in Hawaii. In fact, Hawaii may well be the only whale grounds in the North Pacific where there is no history of commercial whaling. (This is so unusual that some researchers wonder if humpbacks even came to Hawaii during whaling times — the peak humpback whaling era covering the first half of the 1900s. Frankly, this is the most likely explanation for the lack of whaling history.)

Throughout the rest of the North Pacific, however, humpback whale populations, which may have included 'Hawaiian' whales, were subjected to relentless hunting for over fifty years. Indeed, commercial extinction (when commercial whaling operations were no longer viable due to difficulty in finding a whale) occurred in most

Whale watching off Maui began in the 1970s. It was an opportunity for people to see living whales and for the whales to interact with humans not bent on killing them.

I Was the Intruder . . .

"There was not a breath of wind and the sea was glassy calm. . . . I eased off the surfboard. . . . One instant the water was empty. The next, it had substance. A vague, looming shadow became the outline of a tremendous head. . . . All feelings of apprehension vanished. The monster from the depths had appeared, but . . . he was not frightening. In fact he seemed to radiate friendliness. . . . The whale did not change his pace or seem disturbed. But he did roll to one side for a better view of me. . . . I was the intruder, a curiosity from another world."

— Jon Lindbergh
Life magazine, 1967

This may be the earliest published description of an underwater encounter with a 'Hawaiian' humpback (off Lahaina, Maui), several years ahead of general interest in these whales.

regions before international protection. We're not sure how many 'Hawaiian' humpbacks remained by then — a few hundred, maybe.

Then came the 1970s, and our view of whales changed — about as much as it could change. As the decade began, the first killer whales had been brought to aquariums and captured public attention. Then Jacques Cousteau's TV documentaries introduced us all to living whales in their natural habitat. The songs of humpback whales were played around the world on bestselling record albums (and were even sent into space). "Save the Whales" campaigns, with perhaps the first engagement of the mass media in conservation issues, brought the whales' plight to the fore-front. The campaigns of Greenpeace and others received unprecedented coverage and interest. The art, and business, of whale watching truly began. The US Marine Mammal Protection Act was passed. The International Whaling Commission, long charged with the role of managing whaling, also became a forum for protecting whales. The more we got to know the animals as living creatures rather than as carcasses on a whaling ramp or as market commodities, the more our attitudes changed.

In that time and atmosphere, a few brave souls ventured out and slipped into the water with humpback whales. The first underwater photographs and films of whales in the blue, shimmering

Living humpback whales were first filmed in Hawaii in the 1970s, and those images did much to capture public attention. Above, a diver films a passing whale with a huge IMAX camera.

waters of Hawaii changed our perception of the world a little. These images, more than any other single factor, solidified human interest in the living whales.

The decade of the seventies also marked the beginning of an entirely new field of endeavor — the study of living whales in their natural habitat. Until that time, the idea that a researcher could locate and spend enough time with whales at sea to actually learn something about them was thought to be impossible. Research on live whales began with people who didn't know it could not be done. They sought out and spent time close to whales in their natural habitat. Soon it became clear that individual animals could be recognized by natural markings, allowing repeat sightings and extended observation. Within a decade of this discovery, such studies spanned the globe. Hawaii, along with a handful of other locations, was at the forefront of this activity.

The time since the 1970s has been one of unprecedented progress for whale research. With new tools and techniques (such as photo-identification, underwater observation, sophisticated genetic analysis of skin to determine sex and relationships, and high-tech satellite tracking), the horizons of what is possible have been extended over and over. It has been an exciting time for researchers, as virtually everything seen and documented has been new, providing the first real insights into the nature of living whales.

The Finest Natural Laboratory

Whales are found worldwide: along the coastlines of all the continents, around oceanic islands, amidst ice packs in polar seas, and far offshore. All these places are critical to whales. So, why study them in Hawaii? Because, hands down, it is one of the finest natural laboratories in the world.

There are significant challenges to studying wild whales. The top three are probably simply locating whales in the vast reaches of the sea, finding ocean conditions that allow a scientist to be more concerned with the project than survival, and then solving the logistics of spending the days, weeks, and months necessary to get the job done. It is critical that whales be studied in all locations, there is no doubt. However, the closer one is to overcoming these three challenges, the more time there is to explore the nature of the whales themselves.

Humpback whales typically seek out water in the 72–76°F (19–21°C) range for winter assembly. Such locations in the North Pacific are in the zone of the trade winds — so named for their consistency and strength, aiding the passage of sailing ships. In the northern hemisphere

Hawaii's warm, clear, and relatively calm waters make it one of the finest natural laboratories in the world.

'the trades' blow regularly from the northeast, typically at 15–35 knots. This is bad for whale researchers. Attempting to locate, stay close to, and study whales in these ocean conditions can be daunting, as can be attested by humpback researchers in many other locations in the world that have only low-lying or no land masses nearby.

In Hawaii, however, volcanic mountains ranging from 5,000 to 10,000 feet or more (1,500 to 3,000 m) (including the West Maui Mountains and Haleakala on Maui, and Mauna Loa and Mauna Kea on the Big Island) act as giant windbreaks and create calm-water zones (lees) behind them. Calm water is very good for whale research. (The size of the lee changes with wind speed and direction, and it is the first and most important subject of discussion every single morning of the field season.)

Another reason Hawaii is a prime location for whale research is its mid-ocean, subtropical location, which results in remarkable underwater visibility — not uncommonly in the 100-foot (30-m) range.

This visibility is the result of several factors, including a lack of large rivers to pour sediment in the water or supply nutrients for plankton growth — both of which reduce visibility. (However, run-off created from rainfall on agricultural lands does decrease visibility dramatically in the short term.) In Hawaii, the whales can actually be observed beneath the surface and, equally important, they can see us and not be surprised or frightened. Clearly, this is a huge advantage when studying whale behavior.

Last, but not least, are the very practical and logistical considerations that are a large part of any research program:

- How easy is it to reach the study area?
- Are there harbors with boat facilities, fuel, and services?
- What kind of accommodation is available?
- What language is spoken?
- Is it in a war zone?
- Are there medical facilities?
- How difficult is it going to be to actually get researchers on the water?
- What will the cost be?

These are significant limiting factors in many whale research programs around the world. In Hawaii, though, these issues are either relatively easily resolved or do not even arise.

It is the combination of all these things (lots of whales, calm conditions, good visibility, and logistical ease) that makes Hawaii so special in terms of whale research. Simply, it allows a researcher to spend entire days very close to whales, in conditions permitting observation both on the surface and underwater. These circumstances have led to a steady stream of research, photographs, and films, resulting in many first-descriptions, new insights, and new hypotheses on humpback behavior.

These conditions are also ideal for studies of other cetaceans. The list opposite illustrates the many other whales and dolphins that can be seen in Hawaii. Other species of large baleen whales are seen, but sightings are rare and usually fleeting. In contrast, a great variety of toothed whales (including dolphins) live here, with many species found where the banks surrounding the islands drop off into deep water.

Cetaceans in Hawaiian Waters

This list of cetaceans is a composite based on surveys of the Hawaiian Islands that have documented six species of baleen whales and eighteen species of toothed whales. The likelihood of sightings given here only suggests the odds of seeing a particular species during casual boating activities — it does not necessarily represent abundance of the species in Hawaii.

	Season(s) in Hawaii	Sightings
Baleen Whales (Mysticeti)		
Humpback Whale	Winter	Common
Right Whale	Winter	Rare
Minke Whale	Unknown	Rare
Bryde's Whale	Year-round	Rare
Sei Whale	Unknown	Rare
Fin Whale	Unknown	Rare
Toothed Whales (Odontoceti)		
Spotted Dolphin	Year-round	Common
Spinner Dolphin	Year-round	Common
Bottlenose Dolphin	Year-round	Common
False Killer Whale	Year-round	Common
Short-Finned Pilot Whale	Year-round	Common
Rough-Toothed Dolphin	Year-round	Common*
Melon-Headed Whale	Year-round	Common*
Pygmy Killer Whale	Year-round	Common*
Sperm Whale	Spring-Summer	Common*
Striped Dolphin	Year-round	Less Common
Pygmy Sperm Whale	Year-round	Less Common
Dwarf Sperm Whale	Unknown	Less Common
Blainville's Beaked Whale	Year-round	Rare
Cuvier's Beaked Whale	Year-round	Rare
Killer Whale	Unknown	Rare
Fraser's Dolphin	Unknown	Rare
Longman's Beaked Whale	Unknown	Rare
Risso's Dolphin	Unknown	Rare

In certain locations (e.g. Kona) sightings of this species are as stated; elsewhere, chances of seeing it are lower.

How Have We Learned About Humpback Whales?

Scientific understanding of humpback whales has come in two distinct phases: first, from the results of half a century of whaling, and second, from over thirty years of field studies of living whales.

Whaling Studies

GORDON PIKE, DFO CANADA

For many years our knowledge of humpback whales came mostly from carcasses on whaling ramps.

Prior to research on living whales, virtually all we knew about their life history was pieced together from the examination of thousands of dead animals from whaling operations. Intrepid biologists, digging around inside dead whales, examined testes to learn the peak of male breeding activity (spermatogenesis), ovaries to determine female sexual maturity and birth rates, and fetus sizes to estimate birth times. Stomach contents told what they ate and when. The recovery of long metal darts (known as "Discovery tags") shot into whales in other locations determined where they had been prior to being killed.

Reports based on these data appeared from the early 1900s up to the 1960s and provided a valuable framework for understanding reproductive cycles; in fact, they are still used as a basis for studying the behavior of living whales.

Studying Living Whales at Sea

The second phase of whale study began in the 1970s with the first research on living whales in their natural habitat. The value of photo-identification of animals by natural markings to enable repeat sightings of individuals cannot be overstated. It remains the primary tool of living whale research. Close surface and underwater observations and the development of sighting and behavioral histories of individual whales gave rise to the first descriptions of behavior patterns in the wild.

Today, most whale research can be divided into three general approaches:

- *Short-term.* Includes surveys by boat or airplane that record location, numbers, general behavior (traveling, feeding, etc.), and perhaps social groupings. These studies are not based on individual IDs, are relatively short in duration, and provide snapshots of distribution and abundance over the survey area.

Whalers in Hawaii

Although no commercial whaling occurred in Hawaii, it was a popular place for whalers of the 1800s to spend the winter. The actual whaling, for sperm whales, occurred in northern seas in summer.

Lahaina, Maui was a favorite overwintering location, and clashes between whalers and missionaries make for colorful history.

Intriguingly, no mention of humpback whales has been found in the log books of whaling ships anchored in the roadstead off Lahaina. This makes some wonder if their presence in Hawaii in winter is a relatively new phenomenon.

Coincidentally, Lahaina is now the field base of the majority of whale research programs in Hawaii.

- *Long-term.* Includes abundance and distribution studies and all detailed behavior work. These studies are based on identification, repeat sightings, and extensive observations of individual whales. They are conducted over multiple years, even lifetimes, often from small craft and with both surface and under-water observations.

- *Remote.* Includes research on migration and behavior with satellite or other high-tech tags attached to the whales. These studies require relatively little time with the animal directly — just attaching the tag — but potentially huge amounts of time 'watching' remotely.

Due to its power in revealing the gender and relatedness of animals, the study of genetics is arguably a fourth approach in itself. However, it is more often an extra tool used in other studies. Researchers tend to specialize in one of these three approaches, or in genetics, as they all require somewhat different sets of expertise. Of course, ideally all these methods would be used to answer any specific question.

The approach taken to any whale study is determined by the objective — what exactly it is we are trying to learn. For example, common wildlife-management objectives are to estimate population size, map critical habitat, or determine age of sexual maturity and birth rate. In some cases, the objective is to define populations by studying migratory destinations and genetic relationships. In other cases, researchers may be primarily interested in the social organization and behavior of whales and address questions like:

- What is the mating system?
- What are the reproductive strategies of males and females?
- How (and what) do they communicate?
- What is the structure of whale society?

Researchers match the objective to the general approach, and set about designing the study.

Whales can be curious, too.
This whale takes a moment
to check out the researchers.

Many whale studies are conducted from small boats and involve photo-identifying animals and analyzing repeat sightings of individuals over many years. Above, one whale is releasing a stream of bubbles from its blowhole.

Working With Whales

Finding whales in a good study location is not the end to the challenges of studying whale behavior at sea — it's just the beginning. Think for a minute about the factors involved.

First, there is the ocean, which can change from calm to life threatening — at times in a matter of minutes. Then there are the whales themselves, with movements restricted by nothing except the shoreline and physiology, ranging over huge distances. Moreover, they spend 90 percent of their time hidden underwater.

Then there is the assortment of electrotechnical equipment such as digital cameras and recorders, hydrophones (underwater microphones), and GPS units that have become the mainstays of research and must work as they bounce around in damp, salty conditions on small boats. There are the boats themselves, prone to breakdowns and periodic downtime for maintenance.

The flow of a research season often goes something like this: Whales are present, but ocean is impossible; or ocean is calm but the whales are gone; or both whales and ocean are good but the boat breaks down; or everything is working but the rain last night ruined the visibility underwater. (You get the idea.) There are a number of variables, some entirely out of a researcher's control, which have to come together for the work to get done.

Consequently, studies of living whales at sea are long-term endeavors. It simply takes a long time to collect the observations necessary to be able to say anything with any level of scientific certainty. Usually, the more sophisticated the question (the goal is often to learn enough to ask more sophisticated questions), the more variables that need to line up before useful data is obtained, and therefore the more time is needed. Then, when everything works, we are rewarded with just a glimpse into the lives of these animals. To date, our understanding of whales comes from a series of such glimpses.

What Are Researchers Doing Out There?

From shore, or perhaps from a whale-watching boat, small boats may be seen operating very close to the whales. These are researchers. In Hawaii they are required to have federal and state permits to approach whales. The interaction of the researchers with whales (and consequent movements of the boats) depends on what they are trying to accomplish. Following are descriptions of several of the most common activities of researchers in Hawaii, including what may be seen from shore or a whale-watching boat, the technique(s) employed, and the use of the resulting data.

Who Studies Whales in Hawaii?

Hawaii has spawned major research programs. Several initiated in the 1970s and 1980s continue today and now feature over thirty years of continuous observation and data collection. Most studies are multi-year programs exploring larger research questions in stages.

Research is conducted by professional biologists, graduate students, and experienced local researchers, often funded by individuals, non-governmental organizations and charitable foundations.

Individual Identification

What you may see: Research boat maneuvering behind whales. If group is large, or whales are not showing their flukes often, this could continue for hours.

Why? To take identification (ID) photos of individual whales. Each whale is given an ID number and some are even named.

How? Individual humpbacks have unique black-and-white pigment patterns on the underside of their tail flukes. A photograph of these markings provides a permanent ID record of an individual.

What for? ID photos and records of repeat sightings of individuals are the basis of most whale studies today (e.g. for population estimates, local and migratory movement patterns, and behavior studies).

Determining Sex

BILL SCOTT

What you may see: Diver in water; or boat rushing to a breach site then researchers using dip-nets; or boat paralleling a whale to shoot a crossbow dart.

Why? To determine if a whale is male or female.

How? By three techniques: (1) sex-specific behavior (e.g. singers are males, whales with calves are females); (2) arrangement and shape of genital area different from male to female (underwater photo); (3) genetic sex determination from skin sample (sloughed or biopsy).

What for? Knowing the sex of an individual is essential to interpreting behavior patterns and social organization. Genetic analyses also provide information on how whales are related to each other.

Estimating Age

What you may see: Helicopter hovering above a research boat; or boat repeatedly maneuvering to be directly behind whales.

Why? To estimate the age or age class (young, juvenile, adult) of whales.

How? By measuring the size of the whale or some part of it. Photos are taken from the air, surface, or underwater, and size is calculated by photogrammetric comparison. One method is measuring tail flukes (the larger the tail, the larger the whale).

What for? Age data, even relative age estimates (i.e. small, medium, and large whales) are important for the interpretation of social behavior.

Recording Whale Sounds

What you may see: Research boat stationary, engine off, for long periods, occasionally repositioning after a whale surfaces. Or a boat running well ahead of whales stopping, deploying a hydrophone, then remaining stationary as the animals approach.

Why? To record whale songs and social sounds.

How? Sound recordings are made using a hydrophone hanging off the side of the stationary research boat and connected to a recorder.

What for? Sound is a primary sense of whales and is therefore a key to any study of social behavior.

The Research Process

To appreciate the nature of the material in this book requires a few words about the research process. First, it *is* a process — a journey. Researchers begin by knowing little about a topic. In fact, we may have just discovered it exists! Then the scientific work begins, and over time we get closer and closer to an accurate description or understanding of its nature.

During this process we get into the neighborhood of answers. For example, to a question such as "Why do whales breach?" our response would start with field observations like the following:

- Both sexes and all ages of whales breach.
- They breach on breeding grounds and on feeding grounds.
- They breach when alone and in groups.
- They can breach once or many times in succession.
- Whales often breach when they go from calm to windy water.

It can take a long time to answer what seem like the simplest questions about whales. Researchers need to find ways of observing the behavior, develop ideas based on these observations, then test them through scientific studies.

These observations provide us with the context in which they breach. But why do they breach? That we still don't know. The best current guess, considering the observations above, is that it's plain exuberance.

The main point here is that the quality of the answer to any question about whales depends entirely on where the question occurs on the research journey. If near the beginning, the answers researchers supply should be fairly vague, filled with words like initial, preliminary, speculative, or hypothetical. Accept them, because they are likely the best answers we have at the time, but don't take them too much to heart. They may ultimately be proven correct, only partially correct, or even completely wrong! If, on the other hand, the question is asked farther along in the process, with multiple studies completed over a number of years, ideas tested through the scientific process, and with different researchers coming up with the same conclusion, then it means we are getting closer to a definitive answer. With whales, in general, we are fairly early on in the journey.

Humpback Whales

Scientific Name: *Megaptera novaeangliae* (literally, big-winged New Englander). Their common name arose from the arching of their back when diving.

Classification: Humpback whales are one of fifteen species of baleen whales (Mysticeti), divided into four taxonomic families: Eschrichtiidae (gray whales), Balaenidae (right whales), Neobalaenidae (pygmy right whales) and Balaenopteridae (blue, finback, sei, Bryde's, minke, and humpback whales).

Identifying Features: Humpbacks are gray to black with a humplike to sickle-shaped dorsal fin. They have unique, long (15-ft/5-m) black-and-white flippers, distinctive bumps on top of the head, and black-and-white pigment patterns on the underside of the tail flukes.

Size and Weight: Adult, 40–45 feet (12–14 m) and 25–35 tons (estimated). Adult female is larger than male. Newborn calf is 10–15 feet (3–4.5 m) and a yearling is 25–30 feet (8–10 m).

Distribution: Cosmopolitan (worldwide).

Migrations: Migrate annually from high-latitude summer feeding grounds to subtropical or tropical winter breeding grounds.

Food: Larger zooplankton (krill) and a variety of herring-sized fish.

Reproduction: On average one calf every two years.

Life Span: Estimates of 40–80+ years.

Status: On "endangered" lists and protected worldwide, but many populations are recovering. Estimates of numbers: Hawaii 10,000, North Pacific 20,000, world 100,000+.

Humpback whales are easily distinguishable from other large whales by their long black-and-white flippers and knobby heads.

Whales!

Quick Info

What kind of whales are they?

Almost without exception, the whales in Hawaiian waters in winter are humpback whales. Other large whales such as right whales or finbacks are sighted very rarely. A variety of smaller dolphins and other toothed whales live in the area year-round.

What are the humpback whales doing out there?

Hawaiian waters are a breeding ground for humpback whales. So, during the winter, humpbacks migrate to Hawaii to mate and give birth.

Was there ever whaling in Hawaii?

There is no record of commercial whaling in Hawaii. However, during the 1800s, Hawaii (including Lahaina on Maui) was a popular location for whaling ships to spend the winter while waiting for the season to hunt sperm whales in northern seas.

How have we learned about whales?

Our knowledge of whales has come in two distinct phases: (1) studies of dead whales from the whaling industry, mostly ending in the 1960s; and (2) studies of living whales at sea, which began in the 1970s.

How much do we know about whales?

Our scientific understanding of whales is relatively young, with many basic questions still to be answered. However, since the 1970s we have learned more about living whales than in all the previous years combined.

Social Groups
on the Breeding Grounds

Surface Active Group
A surface active group consists of multiple males following a single female (presumably in estrus). Male interaction is predominantly competitive as the female's escort defends his position against challengers.

Singer
A singer is an adult male, usually alone, but at times with another male or female (which may have a calf). He may sing while stationary or traveling.

Joiner
A joiner is a non-singing male that approaches and joins a singer. The singing usually stops as they interact. The whales often split up after a few minutes, but may travel off together.

Surface Active Group (with calf)
Later in the breeding season, the female involved in a surface active group often has a newborn calf by her side. Juveniles are commonly found at the periphery of these groups.

LANAI

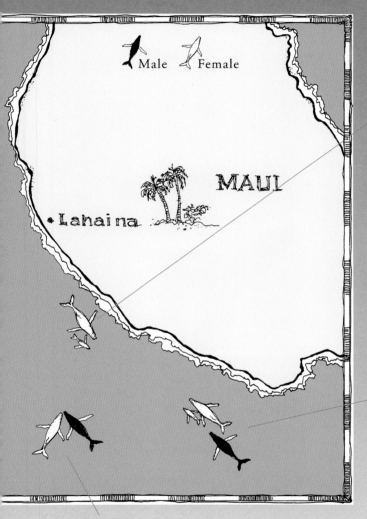

Mother/Calf

Mother/calf pairs may be stationary (resting) or traveling. They are often found in nearshore shallows and do not mix with other mother/-calf pairs. At times a mother is accompanied by her yearling, and occasionally by both newborn and yearling.

Mother/Calf and Escort

Most mother/calf pairs are escorted by a male. The male stays close to the female and defends his position against other males. The female may accept the male's company or, at other times, flee.

Female/Male Pair

Adult female/male pairs are common in the first half of the winter season. Often stationary, they stay close together, remaining submerged for 15–20+ minutes at a time. The male defends his position against other males.

Not shown in the diagram are lone whales (usually males traveling to join other whales), or groups of juveniles.

Chapter 2

'Hawaiian' Humpbacks

In Hawaii, the first sighting of a humpback whale in the fall is an event. It is usually spotted by a snorkeling boat or fisherman (typically in September or October), and it makes the local newspapers. . . . They're back. The progression of events that comprises the breeding season of humpbacks in Hawaii begins.

The Hawaiian Islands are the focal point for whales that have migrated thousands of miles across open ocean. They swing around the islands, most lingering just weeks in the relative shallows (and increasing social density dramatically), then head back towards their feeding grounds.

It is therefore unlikely the whales you see on one day are the same individuals as the day before. The whale situation in Hawaii is very dynamic, with a virtual parade of individual whales through the region. In addition, the predominant social groups (determined by age, sex, and reproductive stage) change as the season progresses.

What are they doing here? Where do they come from? When are they present? Where are the best places to see them? This chapter answers some of these basic questions about the whales we see in Hawaii. And it sets the stage for the more complex question asked by researchers — why do they behave the way they do?

Hawaii — A Migratory Destination

Worldwide, humpback whales migrate annually between food-rich, cold-water summer feeding grounds and subtropical winter grounds where they breed and give birth. There are eleven populations of humpbacks throughout the world's oceans, each with traditional feeding and breeding grounds. Hawaii is one of these breeding grounds.

The humpback whale migratory pathways are typically between higher and lower latitudes along either side of the continents in both the northern and southern hemispheres. There are exceptions, as a humpback whale population off Oman in the Indian Ocean appears not to migrate at all, and Hawaii, needless to say, is in the middle of the largest ocean in the world.

Why Migrate?

Scientists do not yet understand why humpback whales make this annual migration thousands of miles away from their food supply. The shortest distance from Hawaii to Alaska is about 2,700 miles (4,400 km) one way. Humpbacks make a huge seasonal shift, from a context of feeding, resting, and net energy gain, to one of significant energy

Humpback whales make a huge seasonal shift in behavior, from summer feeding and net energy gain (*left*), to winter fasting and major energy expenditure (*right*).

expenditure involving traveling, fasting, birthing, nursing, and mating.

Two key environmental conditions are the same for humpback whale winter assembly areas worldwide: relatively warm water and shallow depth. The temperature of the water in North Pacific breeding grounds ranges from approximately 66–77°F (19–25°C), compared to feeding-ground temperatures of 46–57°F (8–14°C). Breeding grounds are typically situated on shallow banks several hundreds of feet deep, whereas surrounding waters (as well as waters in the feeding grounds) may be thousands of feet deep.

Presumably, these conditions improve the chances of successful reproduction, and perhaps especially serve the needs of mothers with newborn calves. Exactly how these environmental conditions are important to breeding whales is not yet known, although they probably meet both physiological (energetic) and behavioral needs.

Humpback whales that feed in widely separated regions in summer concentrate and mix during the winter assembly. This gathering may therefore promote genetic mixing and diversity, which may be another function of migrations. The concentration of whales on the breeding grounds also makes it easier for them to find each other.

North Pacific Humpback Whale Migrations

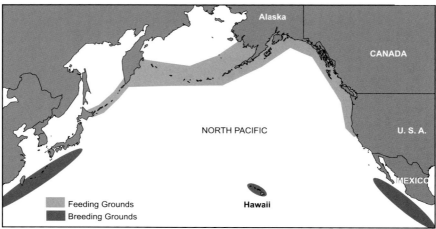

North Pacific humpback whales leave summer feeding grounds around the Pacific Rim (*light shading*) and migrate to three main winter assembly areas in subtropical and tropical waters (*dark shading*).

Humpback whales spend the summer in cold-water feeding grounds around the North Pacific Rim, from California to northern Japan. In late fall and early winter, most leave their summer grounds and migrate to subtropical breeding grounds. In the North Pacific, there are three general regions where humpbacks assemble in the winter: (1) in the eastern North Pacific from Mexico southwards as far as Costa Rica; (2) in the central North Pacific around the main Hawaiian Islands; and (3) in the western North Pacific from southern Japan to Taiwan and the northern Philippines.

Humpback whales on specific feeding grounds are more likely to migrate to one breeding ground over another. Migratory destinations have been determined with three techniques: (1) the use of Discovery tags in the whaling era (metal darts shot into whales and recovered at a later date and location, when the whale was killed and rendered); (2) resightings of photo-identified individual whales; and (3) observations of satellite-tagged whales.

Researchers have learned that:

- Humpback whales that feed from Northern California to Vancouver Island in the summer are almost always found in Mexican and Central American breeding grounds in the winter.

- Humpbacks that feed from Vancouver Island to Alaska in summer are often found in Hawaii in winter, although some migrate to Mexico.

- Humpbacks that feed in the Bering Sea, along the western Aleutian Islands, and along the Russian coast are more likely to be found in the Asian wintering areas.

However, there are marked exceptions to these generalities. Some whales head to breeding areas far distant from that of their summer neighbors. Moreover, individuals have been identified in one breeding ground one year and in another the next! That is, for instance, in Mexico one winter and in Hawaii another winter, or in Japan one year and in Hawaii another year.

It took one whale a maximum of 39 days to migrate between SE Alaska and Hawaii (determined by photo-identification in both locations).

Gabriele et al. 1996

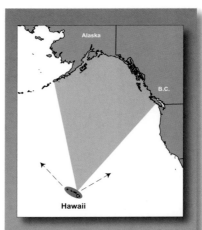

Where Are the 'Hawaiian' Humpbacks in Summer?

Perhaps the best way of thinking about the summer grounds of Hawaiian humpbacks is to picture a piece of pie with the point on Hawaii.

Most humpbacks seen in Hawaii migrate to summer feeding grounds in Alaska and British Columbia (BC).

Numerous individual whales have been photo-identified in both locations, and whales satellite-tagged in Hawaii migrated directly to northern BC and southeast Alaskan waters.

It is, however, important to emphasize that any single humpback seen in Hawaii could potentially spend the summer in just about any location around the Pacific Rim. Indeed, one whale satellite-tagged in Hawaii spent the summer in Russian waters.

JIM DARLING

'Missing' Whales?

Some mature females apparently do not make the entire migration to the breeding grounds each year, presumably due to the high energy costs of migration and reproduction. There is an ongoing discussion among researchers about females 'missing' from the breeding grounds, and it is generally agreed that far more males than females make the migration. Possible reasons include some females taking a 'rest year,' and some females becoming pregnant en route and returning to the feeding grounds instead of continuing to Hawaii.

Currently there is more speculation than hard data on this subject. For example, research on the number, sex, and identity of whales that remain off Alaska during winter does not show that females are in the majority, as might be expected if males are in the majority in Hawaii. So the question of exactly where the 'missing' females are remains open.

Biopsy sampling during the migrations of humpback whales along the east coast of Australia (to and from South Pacific breeding grounds) revealed a sex ratio of 2.4 males to every 1 female.

Brown et al.
1995

MEAGAN JONES

Humpback whales worldwide seek out warm, relatively shallow waters for winter breeding grounds. Hawaii is one such location.

Breeding And Nursery Grounds

Geography or Behavior?

It's convenient to say that humpback whales come to Hawaii to breed and give birth, but that's not strictly true. Reproductive activities begin, and some births occur, before the whales reach Hawaii. In fact, some behavior patterns related to breeding activity, such as singing, begin as early as late fall and before the whales leave their summer feeding grounds. It is apparent that reproductive behavior occurs throughout the southern migration, peaks during the winter assembly in Hawaii, and then continues to some extent on the northern migration back to feeding grounds. For this reason, the geographic boundaries of where breeding behavior occurs (that is, the "breeding grounds") are not easily defined.

Where are the Whales in Hawaii?

Humpback whales are most abundant in a specific habitat in the Hawaiian Islands — they prefer the 'shallow' banks less than 600 feet (180 m) deep that encircle, or in some cases connect, islands. This habitat is in contrast to the deep-water channels up to 6,000 feet (1,900 m) deep and the ocean basin that surround these islands. Therefore, in general, the greater the extent of the shallow banks, the more abundant the whales. However, the whales regularly cross the deep inter-island channels to move between islands.

During aerial surveys, the majority of whales (74%) were found in water of less than about 100 fathoms (600 ft).

Mobley et al.
1994

Whales are found throughout the main Hawaiian Islands in winter, with higher concentrations in certain locations *(dark shading)*.

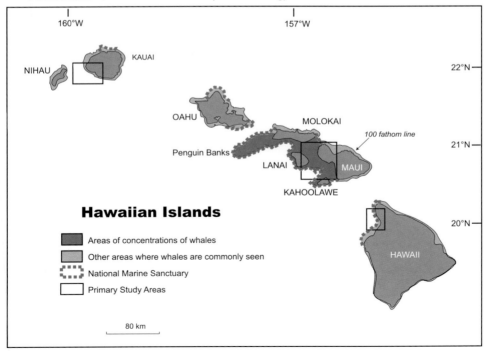

Blows are easy to spot from the West Maui shoreline in late afternoon and evening as the sun sets behind the island of Lanai.

When Is The Best Time To See Whales?

Humpbacks are winter visitors to Hawaii. They are most abundant from mid-December through early April, with peak numbers in February and March. Humpbacks have been seen as early as September and as late as June, but sightings before November or after May are rare.

The most common whale groupings vary over the course of the season. That is, whale watchers in January are likely to see different types of groups than whale watchers in March. This is partly due to staggered arrival and departure times of whales based on their age, sex, and reproductive stage.

Our knowledge of the order of the migration (and the arrival and departure from the breeding grounds) comes primarily from studies conducted during whaling operations in different parts of the world. It was discovered that if whaling occurred throughout an entire season on humpback breeding grounds, then the status of the whales caught changed (in terms of age, sex, and reproductive stage). These studies

The type of whale group most likely to be seen on the breeding grounds changes as the season progresses due to migratory order and reproductive status. For example, in the early season, adult male/female pairs (*above*) are very common; later, mothers with a calf and male escort (*below*) predominate.

41

suggest the migratory order to and from the breeding grounds as follows, with a degree of overlap among the groups.

Arrival Order	**Departure Order**
1st Females with yearling	1st Mature females**
2nd Immature whales	2nd Immature whales
3rd Mature (resting*) females	3rd Mature males
4th Mature males	4th New mothers
5th Females in late pregnancy	

* Ovaries and mammary glands showed no signs of recent activity.
**Newly pregnant or in a rest year.

This sequence found by whalers (mostly in the southern hemisphere) is somewhat confirmed by observations in Hawaii. Juveniles and adult pairs (presumably male/female) without a calf are common in December, January, and early February; the numbers of new mothers with a calf increases after February 1 and through March; and mothers with newborn calves are the last to depart in April and May. At the peak of the season, all age, sex, and reproductive categories are present.

A procession of humpback whales passes through the Hawaiian Islands in winter, most lingering in the relatively shallow waters for several weeks.

How Long Does Any Individual Whale Stay In Hawaii?

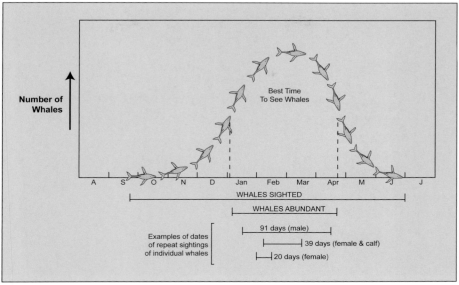

Humpback whales are abundant in Hawaii between December and April, with peak numbers in February and March. Most individual whales stay in Hawaii for relatively short periods (weeks), but some males stay much longer (months).

So far, we have a picture for when whales are most abundant and when different age, sex, and reproductive classes may arrive and depart. In addition, studies suggest that most individual whales do not spend the whole season in Hawaii, and in fact are present for relatively short periods of the overall humpback season.

This insight comes primarily from the number of days or weeks between resightings of photo-identified individuals. When researchers compare all the identification pictures taken in one season, they find within-year

There is, so to speak, a marching column in the migration of whales.

Nishiwaki 1962

43

Repeat sightings of individual whales (identified by photographs of the permanent skin pigment patterns on the underside of the flukes) allow estimates of the length of their stay in Hawaii.

matches — whales seen more than once. For example, Whale #971 may have been seen on February 5, February 12, and March 15, with a total time between first and last sightings of thirty-nine days *(see chart on page 43)*.

These analyses suggest that most individual whales arrive, spend about a month to six weeks in Hawaii, then leave just as other individuals arrive in succession, and so on. There is, however, a possible exception to this pattern — some males may spend a significantly longer time in the region than other males and females. This suggestion is supported by three pieces of information. (1) All whales of known sex present over more than eight weeks are males. (2) The longest periods of repeat sightings of males are about three months, or the length of the peak season. (3) There are several examples of the same individual males repeating their long stays from year to year. In contrast, the longest period between repeat sightings of females is about seven weeks *(see chart on page 43)*.

The weak point in these analyses is that the study areas where the photo-identifications are taken are small relative to the whole Hawaiian range *(see map on page 39)*. Therefore, it is possible that individuals not seen anymore and presumed to have returned to the feeding grounds could simply be outside the study area but still present in the Islands. The reason researchers don't think this is the case is that several different studies have arrived at the same conclusion for individual length of stay — for instance, satellite tags have indicated whales tagged in Hawaii early in the season may return to the feeding areas before most whales even reach Hawaii, and whales (thought to be a succession of different individuals) are seen on the feeding grounds throughout the winter.

Another study used a mathematical model based on the expected number of repeat sightings of individuals to estimate population size. It found more repeat sightings than expected for a small sub-population of the whales. Apparently, these individuals remained in the area for longer than average (creating a greater chance of them being resighted). The researchers speculated that this subgroup may be mature and perhaps dominant males. These whales may remain longer to maximize opportunities to mate, although this has yet to be proven.

Although whales were present off Maui over five months or more, 88% of repeat sightings of individuals were within six weeks, and the majority within two weeks. All 17 whales (of known sex) resighted over more than six weeks were males.

Darling
1983

The mean 'residence' time for 16 satellite-tagged whales in Hawaii is 13.4 days, but arrival time (in Hawaii) is unknown.

Mate et al.
2007

JIM DARLING

During their stay in the region, individual whales circulate freely between the main Hawaiian Islands.

Whale Movements Within The Hawaiian Islands

Studies based on photo-identification and satellite-tagging now suggest that the norm for all social classes of whales is to circulate throughout the main Hawaiian Island chain, with no animals remaining in one specific area for very long.

One early study proposed a more organized movement where whales entered the Hawaiian chain at the southern end of the Big Island (Hawaii) and generally moved through the region southeast to north-west, eventually leaving from Kauai. This was based on whale counts in the 1980s that seemed to indicate a shift in highest whale densities in this direction as the winter season progressed. However, photo-identified whales were subsequently found moving in the reverse direction (northwest to southeast), from Maui to the Big Island, and Kauai to the Big Island, indicating a one-way flow was not an accurate picture. More recently, satellite tags have revealed whales circulating (seemingly at random) throughout the main island chain. This satellite-tracking study also noted that Kauai may be a northward migration departure point. Hence, there remains some speculation that individuals may make a final move to the northwest before departing.

Nine whales moved one way from Hawaii to Kauai and six moved the reverse direction from Kauai to Hawaii, i.e., no directional trend. The shortest inter-island movement time was eight days.

Cerchio et al.
1998

This map shows the results of three studies of whale movements within Hawaii. Studies A and B are based on photo-identification matches, study C is a satellite-tag track. Study A shows short-term moves back and forth between the Big Island (Hawaii) and Maui; B shows within-season travels from the Big Island to Kauai and the reverse; and C (based on a satellite-tag track) shows one tagged whale that traveled extensivey in a 10-day period.

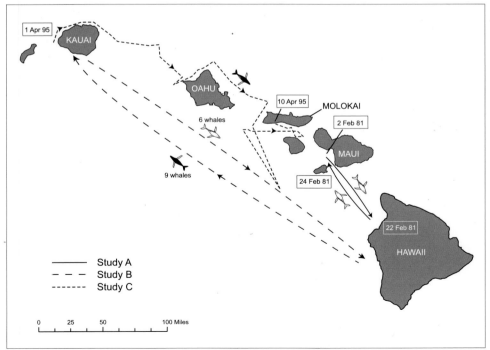

Is There Location-Specific Activity In The Islands?

There is a twofold picture emerging — no social/behavioral boundaries within the main Hawaiian Islands and high mobility throughout the islands by all social groups (possibly some more than others). However, despite this mounting evidence, some researchers continue to speculate that the whales behave differently in different places.

There was an early (1980s) suggestion that some degree of segregation occurs between whales wintering off different islands — that is, different individuals migrate to different islands. This idea is certainly no longer viable. However, the notion persists that the predominant social groups and related behavior patterns may vary to some extent among certain locations. Recently, one research group suggested that the distribution of females in Hawaiian waters may depend on

A humpback leaps from the water just yards off a West Maui shore.

reproductive status, with females more likely to be accompanied by calves off Maui than off the Big Island of Hawaii.

The idea that whales are more likely to be engaged in a type of activity in one location versus another has not been proven. If it does occur, one might expect it to be related to specific habitat conditions (i.e. physical attributes of an area such as shallowness) regardless of where these are rather than to specific geographic locations.

One whale, tracked by satellite tag, traveled at least 820 km in ten days (a mean of 80 km/day) through the coastal waters of five of the Hawaiian Islands: Kauai, Oahu, Molokai, and through Penguin Bank and the Kalohi Channel between Molokai, Maui, and Lanai.

Mate et al.
1998

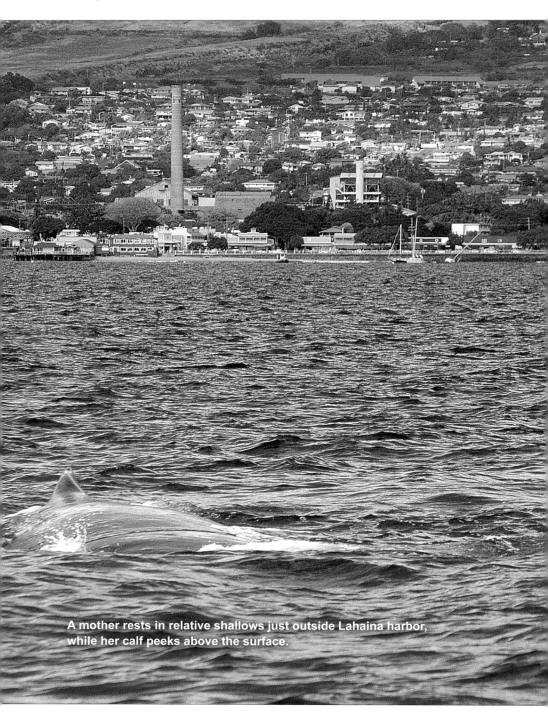

A mother rests in relative shallows just outside Lahaina harbor, while her calf peeks above the surface.

The clearest case of habitat preference is that mothers with young calves are consistently found in shallower, more in-shore waters than most of the population *(see Chapter 6)*. They are not, however, found only in shallow waters or in one region within the islands, so researchers have not been able to define specific nursery areas or conditions. In fact, mothers with calves move throughout the island chain, and are regularly sighted on Penguin Bank *(see map on page 39)*, which has some of the roughest off-shore water in the area.

Humpback whales worldwide seek out warm, relatively shallow waters in winter for mating and birth. Hawaii is the largest breeding ground for this species in the North Pacific, with many of the whales migrating from feeding grounds along the northwest coast of North America. From December through April, humpbacks are abundant around the main Hawaiian Islands, but most individual whales are present for just a small portion of the overall season. There is constant movement and circulation of individuals throughout the island chain, probably dictated by social interactions. Now, the next question for researchers is, why do they behave this way?

'Hawaiian' Humpbacks

Quick Info

Why are the whales in Hawaii?

Humpback whales migrate to Hawaii to mate and give birth. They make long migrations between colder summer feeding grounds and subtropical winter breeding areas. Hawaii is the largest breeding ground for humpbacks in the North Pacific.

Why migrate?

Scientists do not really understand why the whales migrate thousands of miles from their feeding grounds each year. It is apparent that environmental conditions of relatively warm water and comparatively shallow ocean depths (as in Hawaii) are important to reproductive success in humpback whales.

Where do they come from?

Humpback whales that spend the summer feeding along the coastline from Vancouver Island to Alaska are most likely to migrate to Hawaii in winter.

Do all humpback whales migrate each year?

There is evidence that not all mature females make the migration, or at least the entire migration, each year. It is thought that females in a resting (non-reproductive) year, or those that become pregnant en route, may not show up on the breeding grounds.

When is the best time to see humpbacks in Hawaii?

Humpback whales are common in Hawaii from December through April, with peak abundance in February and March.

Where is the best location to see whales in Hawaii?

Humpback whales can be sighted around all the main Hawaiian Islands. The highest densities of whales are within the Four Island Group of Maui, Molokai, Lanai, and Kahoolawe, and on Penguin Bank off the northwestern tip of Molokai. Whales are a little less concentrated but still plentiful off the Kona coast of Hawaii and around Kauai.

How long does an individual whale stay in Hawaii?

Most individual whales stay for short periods of time (several weeks) relative to the overall five- to six-month season, with other individuals arriving in succession as they leave. Some individual males may stay on the breeding grounds for most of the season.

How do whales move locally and use the area?

Individual whales appear to circulate freely around all the main Hawaiian Islands, and rarely stay in a specific location for any length of time.

Chapter 3

Breeding Season

Why do whales behave like they do in Hawaii? Why do they form the kinds of groups we see, such as mothers with newborn calves accompanied by a male escort, or groups of multiple males chasing one female? Why do they sing, and fight, and cooperate? The answers all lie, ultimately, in the female humpback whale's biology.

During the winter, a portion of female humpbacks come into relatively brief periods of heightened sexual receptivity called estrus (known as "heat" in domestic animals). Humpbacks are seasonally polyestrus, undergoing several estrus cycles during a single winter season until successfully pregnant.

Males organize and behave to take advantage of this pattern of female availability and receptiveness. The force behind male behavior on the breeding grounds is not complicated — the urge to mate with as many females as possible — and, as in most mammal societies, their role in reproduction is fleeting.

For females, on the other hand, successful mating leads to a two-year time and energy commitment. The female must nourish the fetus for a year, then give birth, then support the newborn for up to another year. Her success depends on sufficient, and efficient, energy budgeting. It's serious business, and her behavior reflects this.

A humpback female (*center*) juggles newborn care and male attention during the breeding season.

Seasonal Cycles Of Humpback Whales

There are three interrelated cycles that determine the behavior of the female — and hence the male — humpback whale.

- A humpback's year is divided between a feeding season in the summer (includes spring, summer, fall) and a breeding season in winter. In the high latitudes, humpback food (krill and small fish) is abundant in the summer season, but by comparison rare in winter. The humpbacks therefore feed continually when food is available, and shift to mating and birthing when it is not. There is, apparently, an advantage to carrying out the latter in warmer waters, so they migrate.

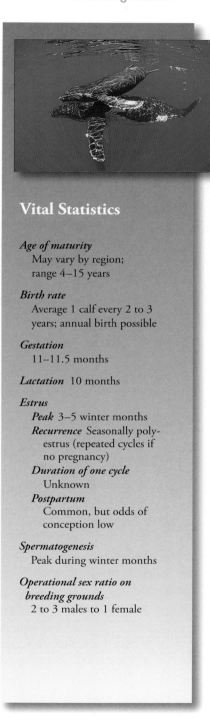

- Humpback whales have a specific reproductive cycle with the same components as all mammals: mating, gestation, birth, and nurturing young. The time between these points in the cycle, as well as the timing and duration of events, is determined by evolutionary and ecological forces. The typical reproductive cycle of a mature humpback is: mating in winter, a year's gestation, birth of one baby during the following (second) winter, a year's care of the baby prior to weaning, then separation in the third winter followed by mating again.

- Within this general pattern, individual females have their own cycles, with estrus occurring at different times and frequencies dependent on condition and age. In North Pacific humpback whales, females collectively come into estrus over the six winter months, but any individual female may be receptive for just a short period during that season or may come into estrus several times if she does not become pregnant the first time. (The sexual cycles of males, with varying production of sperm, tend to reflect the timing of the female breeding season.)

Vital Statistics

Age of maturity
May vary by region; range 4–15 years

Birth rate
Average 1 calf every 2 to 3 years; annual birth possible

Gestation
11–11.5 months

Lactation 10 months

Estrus
Peak 3–5 winter months
Recurrence Seasonally poly-estrus (repeated cycles if no pregnancy)
Duration of one cycle
Unknown
Postpartum
Common, but odds of conception low

Spermatogenesis
Peak during winter months

Operational sex ratio on breeding grounds
2 to 3 males to 1 female

The male in the foreground is escorting or guarding this stationary female, who is likely in or near estrus.

Underwater observation and photography of mothers with newborn calves have advanced our understanding of humpback whale reproductive behavior. (Federal and state permits are required to swim with whales in Hawaii.)

How Have We Learned About Humpback Reproductive Cycles?

Beyond our noticing when females have young calves (versus older calves or yearlings), our understanding of humpback reproduction has been pieced together from three sources:

- Examination of the reproductive organs of dead whales. Large-scale whaling operations in the first half of the 1900s led to tens of thousands of whales being examined. The resulting information has provided much of the framework of humpback reproductive biology.

- Records of birth histories of individual females seen and photo-identified annually. In some cases, a particular female was photo-identified first as a calf, and then sighted each year until she had her own first calf, providing information on age of sexual maturity.

- Male behavior patterns that suggest females are in or near estrus. Simply, the more males and the greater the activity levels around a female, the more likely she is in estrus (or so we assume).

One Hawaii humpback mother had four calves in four sequential years and seven in 11 years.

Glockner-Ferrari and Ferarri 1995

The photo-identification of mothers (such as this one with a tiny newborn calf at her side) and repeat sightings over many years provide insight into birth rates.

JIM DARLING

The best way of estimating age of sexual maturity of a living whale is establishing when a female of known age has her first calf. This is achieved by first photo-identifying females when just a calf and then annually until they produce their first offspring.

Sexual Maturity And Birth Rate

Our understanding of the onset of sexual maturity (estimated by the age a female has her first calf), and then birth rate, is incomplete. Research has provided a range of age of maturity and the main birth patterns, but there remain some key questions to be resolved.

As mentioned above, the two means of estimating age of sexual maturity are from data on whaled specimens and from analyses of living females identified since birth who later produced their own calf. The whaling studies (primarily from the southern hemisphere) estimated age of sexual maturity at 4–6 years based on examination of ovaries. A North Atlantic research project on living whales indicated that the humpbacks have their first calf from 5–7 years of age, which appears to agree with the whaling studies. However, in some contrast to this, a similar study in Alaska indicates that humpbacks there do not have a first calf until 8–16 years, twice the age of the North Atlantic sample! (Further, Alaskan researchers raise questions about the method of age determination in the whaling studies, suggesting it could be off by half.)

So, the available information suggests that humpback females in the North Pacific are twice as old as those in the North Atlantic before having a first calf. This is presently a challenge for researchers, who must explain why age of maturity would differ to this degree. It may be the result of a different ecology between oceans or differing impacts on the populations from whaling.

Once a female has reached sexual maturity, the average birth rate is one calf every two to three years. This rate varies from one female to another and within the same individual over time. Most females are on a two-year cycle with mating one year, birth the next, and so on. Some females, by choice or circumstance, have a resting year in the sequence so that their birth rate may be once every three years.

This pattern seems to make sense considering the energy cost of pregnancy and nursing the calf. It would appear the optimum situation for a mother is not to have both occurring simultaneously. Think of a 10–12 month gestation (nutrition of the fetus) period over-lapping the same period as lactation (production of milk for the newborn). This is not likely to favor the strongest and healthiest offspring.

Female humpback whales of known age in the Gulf of Maine produced first observed calves at ages ranging from 5–7.

Clapham
1992

The age distribution of eleven mothers with their first calf in southeastern Alaska was 8–16 years (mean 11.8 years).

Gabriele et al.
2007

Five (different) humpback whale females (observed in Alaska) successfully demonstrated annual reproduction.

Straley et al.
1994

However, there is also clear evidence for the occurrence of annual birth. This means that the female gives birth and mates the same year (in a matter of weeks of each other!) with the newborn in the midst of the mating activity. Simultaneous gestation and lactation obviously occurs successfully at least in some cases.

What triggers this supercharged annual reproduction is not yet known, although healthy females (the result of high-quality abundant food) is surely part of the formula. This apparent flexibility in birth rate may well be the key to the strong recovery of humpback whale populations relative to certain other baleen whale species.

Estimates of the age of sexual maturity range considerably with different populations of humpback whales. This figure represents the mating/birth pattern of an Alaskan humpback female that first mates at age eight and has a calf at age nine. Note that sometimes a female gives birth and mates in the same winter.

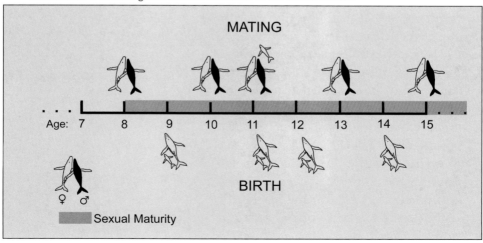

A female producing a calf in consecutive years is relatively uncommon (requiring mating shortly after giving birth). However, males commonly pursue, escort, and compete for mothers with newborn calves, indicating estrus occurs during this time.

When Mating Behavior and Pregnancies Don't Add Up

Largely due to the very common behavioral observation of males escorting a mother with newborn calf, researchers have puzzled over the relative rarity of an annual birth. Male escorts are found in about 85 percent of encounters with mothers and calves. On one hand, the near-universal behavior of males accompanying and competing for mothers with newborn calves strongly suggests that it is common for females to undergo estrus shortly after giving birth. On the other, studies of hunted whales suggest that only a small portion (one estimate indicates 8.5 percent, another 14.4 percent) of mature females conceive annually.

This apparent contradiction has a couple of working explanations. One researcher suggests that ovulation after birth is a common event in female humpback whales (thereby accounting for the male behavior), but that only a portion of these females can maintain pregnancies, dependent on the individual's current physical condition (accounting for the relative rarity of annual birth). There are examples in other mammals that mate soon after giving birth where the embryo may or may not develop beyond a certain stage depending on the mother's and current newborn's health. Another researcher speculates that males may escort females with a calf only after the more reproductively promising females leave Hawaii. In other words, the male's chances of this association leading to offspring are slim, but better than none at all.

JIM DARLING

Groups of males chasing and aggressively competing for access to a female suggests she is in estrus.

Mating Time

Estrus: Occurrence, Recurrence, and Duration

Recall that the humpback whale food supply is primarily available in summer months, which has led to non-feeding, reproductive behavior occurring in winter. Studies during the whaling era indicated that the peak of the sexual cycle in humpback whales in general occurs during the three-to-five winter months. In the North Pacific, one study on sexual cycles based on whales hunted in Japan in the 1950s and 60s determined the peak of female estrus to be in February. This timing matches well with the peak abundance of whales and male engagement with females in Hawaii *(see chart on page 68)*.

Again, however, it may not be quite this clear cut. Several studies in other locations, also based on examination of ovaries, indicate that successful pregnancies can occur well out of synchronization with the majority. One examination of humpback whale fetuses in the North Pacific suggests that successful mating can occur in eleven or even twelve months of the year, with two apparent peaks, one in the February–April period and the other in September! This potentially wide range of timing of mating, conception, and subsequent birth has not been substantiated by recent studies and is rarely emphasized in the literature. However, occasional sightings of humpbacks in Hawaii

Estrus Cycles

Estrus is the period of sexual receptivity in female mammals commonly known as "heat" in domestic animals. It is often affected by seasons, and more specifically by the hours of daylight, which govern the release of key hormones. During estrus, ovulation — the production of eggs — occurs, and pregnancy will likely result from mating activity. These hormones greatly affect behavior. The critical question is timing: how often does the cycle of estrus then anestrus (no estrus) repeat itself, and how long does the estrus period of maximum receptivity last? Virtually nothing is known about this subject in baleen whales. However, an example from domestic sheep (curiously enough) provides some insight into the nature of the cycle.

> *Most female sheep (ewes) are seasonally polyestrus* [yes, the same phrase used to describe humpback whales] *and short-day breeders* [sexually active in fall or winter, also likely the case for humpback whales]. *They will begin to exhibit estrus when the length of day begins decreasing. They* [the sheep] *will come into heat every 16–17 days, which lasts 1–2 days, until they are bred or return to anestrus. The natural time for sheep to breed in the northern hemisphere is in the fall, October or November. When mature ewes are in heat, they will seek out the ram and stand still for him to mount them. Sometimes they wag their tails vigorously or may nuzzle the ram.*
>
> — Susan Schoenian

Sheep may seem a distant subject to whales, but in fact they are not. The extant (currently living) mammals most closely related (genetically) to whales are the Artiodactyls — even-toed ungulates (hoofed animals) that include sheep.

*The peak
of ovulation (in
humpbacks whaled in
Okinawa, Japan)
occurred between the
end of January and the
end of February.*

**Nishiwaki
1959**

in September and October (purposes unknown), and large calves present early in the winter season (January–February), clearly born weeks or even months earlier, make it prudent not to rule out this possibility.

As mentioned earlier, humpback females come into estrus and ovulate seasonally, and during that season may have several cycles. The duration of a single humpback estrus period, or time between multiple cycles, is not known. Our knowledge of this is so scant that one observation in Hawaii of the same female leading competitive groups of males on both February 1 and 6 (1980) may be the best (however circumstantial) indication that estrus extended over a six-day period.

The figure below is based on records of multiple males competing over a single female (presumably in estrus). The male focus on females without calves peaks several weeks before similar behavior around mothers with calves. This analysis suggests estrus in humpback whales occurs from December to April, with a peak in February–March.

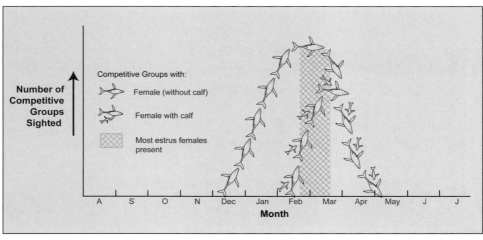

A mother with her newborn calf (*center*) is pursued by several males. This type of group peaks in March and suggests the mother is in postpartum (shortly after birth) estrus.

Male Behavior Indicates Female Estrus

Our only insight into the timing and duration of estrus for humpback whales specifically in Hawaiian waters (where there is no data from whaling) are behavioral observations of extreme male interest in, and competition over, females. In practice, this means researchers record when multiple males are seen competing for a female and make an assumption that this activity means the female is in estrus.

In Hawaii, this competitive behavior has been documented from December

Based on the occurrence and relative numbers of surface active groups, the most estrus females without a calf occurred through February and March, several weeks earlier than the peak number of estrus females with a young calf.

**Darling
1983**

Competitive groups around a female without calf were most frequent from 9 February to 19 March, whereas groups around a female with a calf peaked from 19 February to 1 April. The overlap in these dates is the height of breeding activity.

Gabriele
1992

to May, suggesting estrus females are present in Hawaii over these six months. These groups are most common from mid-January to mid-April. The peak occurrence of males following females without a calf occurs in February and March, which is several weeks earlier than the peak of males pursuing females with a young calf.

This height of (presumed) estrus activity correlates well with the timing of other behavioral indicators such as peak transience of whales in groups (or the shortest period that males stay in one group), aggressive encounters, and singing. (It also correlates well with dates of peak ovulations estimated from data from hunted whales.)

This male escort is chasing a female (with calf) at high speed and lifting her flukes with his head. Males have been observed to rush in directly under a female's tail stock (and genital area) then back off to typical escort position — perhaps checking her state of estrus?

JIM DARLING

How Do Males Know a Female Is Ready to Mate?

We do not know how male whales determine a female is ready to mate. In land mammals, females release scents, give visual clues such as swelling of sexual organs, or change behavior to make themselves available to, or actively pursue, males. In whales we do not know what role, if any, smell (or taste) may play as little is known about these senses in baleen whales. It seems unlikely that visual clues are important in the ocean, as a male virtually has to run into a female to see her! So, for humpbacks, the third mammalian possibility, of females changing their behavior and making sure males find them, may be a large part of the answer.

What We See And Why

It is interesting (and important) to explore the cause of much of the whale action seen in Hawaiian waters.

The most exciting whale behavior for whale watchers is groups of males chasing and fighting over a female. The reason this occurs is that the majority of females give birth every two or three years, so many are not available each breeding season — though there are equal numbers of males and females in the population overall. This results in an *operational* sex ratio of two to three males for every female. The males, therefore, compete for the relatively few receptive females.

Another example is that mothers with a newborn calf are usually accompanied by an adult male escort. This grouping exists because the mother undergoes a postpartum estrus, attracting the males.

Also, the very fact that the whale season in Hawaii extends over five or six months (meaning one can see whales December through April) is the result of the spread of estrus times of individual females.

In every case, the behavior of whales in Hawaii is a consequence of the female reproductive cycle.

Groups of agitated males competing for a receptive female make for good whale watching.

Humpback whales behave as they do in Hawaii because it works. The social groups, actions, and interactions occurring lead to successful pregnancies and offspring — otherwise they would not happen. Patterns of female availability and receptiveness are determined by their physiology and are linked to broader ecological factors. In turn, male behavior has evolved in response to these female patterns. Much of the information in the next few chapters describes the behavior that makes humpback whale reproduction successful.

Breeding Season

Quick Info

What ultimately determines whale behavior in Hawaii?

The distribution of sexually receptive females, in time and space, directs male mating strategies and specific behavior.

When is sexual maturity?

The best information to date, derived from when a female of known age has her first calf, suggests age of sexual maturity varies with location and population of humpback whales (range 4–15 years old).

How often do females give birth?

The average birth rate for a humpback whale is one calf every two to three years. However, some females may produce a calf each year for up to four sequential years.

When do female humpbacks come into estrus?

Female humpback whales typically come into estrus during the winter months, with a peak in the North Pacific from January to March. Each individual female comes into estrus for short periods during that time and either becomes pregnant or repeats the cycle.

How do males know a female is in estrus?

We do not know the answer to this question. From studies of land mammals, it's likely the females provide some form of signal, either through a discharge the males can sense and/or by changing their behavior to make themselves available to males.

How do males react to female sexual cycles?

All male behavior patterns on the breeding grounds (including time of arrival and length of stay) are probably governed by the female cycles. For example, there are more mature males than receptive females present on the breeding grounds at any one time, hence male/male competition occurs for the limited females.

Why do males escort females with a newborn calf?

The females come into estrus shortly after giving birth — hence the male attention. Researchers hypothesize that while estrus and ovulation occur at this time, few successful pregnancies result (but then the males do not know this!).

Chapter 4

Mating — The Male Perspective

Mating, needless to say, is a major item on the agenda of whales in Hawaii. Indeed, it is the only item for males. In any mating situation there are reciprocal male and female behavior patterns, as both want to succeed. However, there is conflict between individual males, each attempting to maximize number of matings, and conflict between the males and a female, who needs to make the most of her mating opportunity — meaning mating with a strong (healthy) male while using up as little energy as possible.

The behavioral story revolves around the fact that there are more sexually mature males than receptive females present at any one time — potentially a lot more. This is good for females, but perhaps not so good for males. To mate, a male must first locate a receptive female, then he must outmaneuver (or otherwise come to terms with) other males that are equally interested in (and willing to fight over) her, and then face the issue of whether or not she will accept him as a suitable mate.

The strategies and behavior involved — from singing complex songs, to stunning battles that can leave blood streaming from head, back, or tail, to teamwork that challenges behavioral theory — are the subject of this chapter.

Male behavior on the breeding grounds is often overt. This male, accompanying a female, makes his displeasure clear (with a vigorous display of bubbles from his blowhole) at the approach of another male.

Singing, Escorting, Competing, And (Perhaps) Cooperating

Male humpback whales in Hawaii are found alone, with other males, and in associations and interactions with females. In this chapter, male behavior patterns are divided into two sections:

- Male/male behavior, which includes singing and joining singers — at times forming male pairs, or larger all-male groups.

- Male behavior around a female, which includes:

    (a) Male/female pairs, when a single male escorts an adult female.

    (b) Multiple male/single female interactions that involve males competing, or cooperating, to gain access to the female.

In Hawaii, most male interactions and associations (both with other males and with females) appear short-lived, lasting only minutes to hours. Then the males move on to the next interaction. A 'long' association might have a male paired with a female (with or without a calf) for a day or so. There is one report of a mother/yearling pair that was escorted by the same male over two days. Whereas researchers agree that males orient to any female in estrus, there is less agreement as to the nature of male/male relations. Most of the earlier literature on this subject suggests males either avoid each other or fight. However, more recent studies have indicated that non-agonistic (friendly) male/male interactions are common, and may even lead in some cases to temporary cooperative unions.

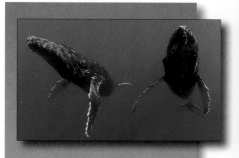

The sex of a total of 22 joiners [of singers] was determined, 14 genetically, eight by behavior. All were males.

Darling and Bérubé
2001

Bulletin: No One Has Actually Seen Mating!

Any discussion of mating behavior must begin with this caveat — there is no documented observation of humpback whale copulation in Hawaiian waters to date. Even with untold thousands of observer hours each season, for more than thirty years, it has not been recorded. (In other species of baleen whales, copulation is commonly observed.) On the other hand, the circumstantial evidence that mating occurs is overwhelming.

This strange situation leaves us guessing as to when and in which behavior pattern or social group copulation actually occurs, what behavior precedes and follows it, or if an individual animal mates once or many times during the season. And, of course, it makes any discussion of mating behavior unavoidably speculative.

Male/Male Behavior

Singing

Male humpback whales sing songs — a complex series of sounds repeated over and over. Singing apparently coincides with the breeding season. Bits of song have (rarely) been recorded in summer, but singing begins in earnest on the fall and early winter feeding grounds, occurs through the migration, likely peaks in the winter assembly, and then falls off in the spring.

Humpback whale song can be heard anytime, anywhere around Hawaii in winter with a hydrophone, or without one virtually anytime one goes swimming and dives beneath the surface along the shoreline. Near a singer underwater, it is about as loud as a home stereo turned up full-blast. In fact, the song is so loud it can be heard emanating from the ocean on a quiet day. Although the amount of singing in a given area may change through the day (and night), singers provide a continual acoustic background to the breeding grounds.

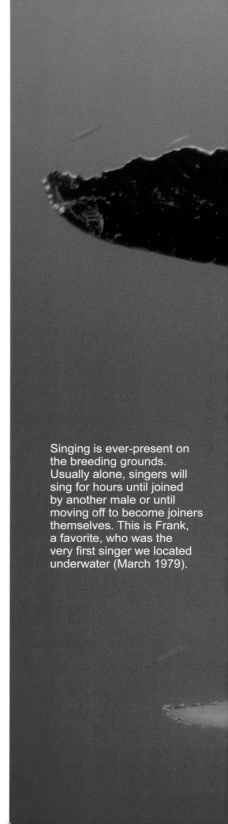

Singing is ever-present on the breeding grounds. Usually alone, singers will sing for hours until joined by another male or until moving off to become joiners themselves. This is Frank, a favorite, who was the very first singer we located underwater (March 1979).

Humpbacks emit sounds in long, predictable patterns ranging over frequencies audible to humans.

**Payne and McVay
1971**

When singing, the whale takes several breaths then dives, leaving a circular slick on the surface. Often, as shown in inset, the singer simply stops 20–40 feet (7–13 m) directly below the slick and at about a 45-degree angle, nose down and tail up.

Here is what is known about singing humpback whales:

- Singing is a male behavior pattern. To date, there has been no record of a female singing.

- Singers are most often lone adult whales. In a minority of encounters, the singer has an adult companion that may be either male or female (at times with calf; that is, the escort accompanying a mother with a calf is singing). There have been a few observations of smaller, juvenile whales near a singer. It is not known at what age males begin singing, but it is presumed to relate to sexual maturity.

- Singers are often stationary (in Hawaiian waters) in what has become known as a singing posture, with tail up and head down at an angle of about forty-five degrees. The tail of the singer is usually about 20–40 feet (7–13 m) beneath the surface. (In some breeding grounds, singers hold this posture with their tail above the surface of the sea.) Whales may also sing while moving around the breeding grounds, as well as during migrations.

- Singing typically continues until: (1) the singer is joined by another whale(s), usually a lone adult male, but occasionally a pair; or (2) the singer stops to join a passing group that includes a female — either a competitive group composed of a female and several males, a male/female pair, or a mother and calf with or without an escort.

The amount of singing increased significantly at night off West Maui.

Au et al.
2000

Bermuda and Whale Song

"Suddenly, I was startled by a loud, low-frequency moan which boomed over the loudspeaker. . . . My imagination soared and I couldn't wait to discover the source."*

— **Frank Watlington**
Bermuda, April 1952

There is no doubt our species has been aware of humpback songs since the first mariner. However, it was not until the 1950s that the first recordings were made — inadvertently.

Frank Watlington, while manning an early underwater listening station in Bermuda, was among the first to realize the source of these sounds.

Watlington's humpback recordings became the main resource for researchers Roger Payne and Scott McVay, who introduced whale songs to the world in 1971 (in the journal *Science*).

* In Bermuda Zoological Society 1983, from Dietz 1982.

The Song

Song Structure

The humpback whale song is a series of sounds that typically lasts 10–15 minutes and is repeated over and over.

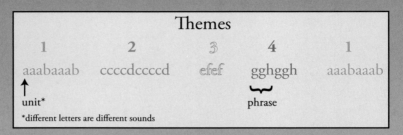

The song consists of several different *themes* (often four to six) sung in a continuous loop. Each theme is composed of sound *units* distinctly arranged as a *phrase*, which is repeated for several minutes. The singer progresses through each of the themes (all with different unit/phrase compositions) until he has worked through the entire song. If the song has four themes the whale will sing Themes 1-2-3-4, usually surface to breathe, then dive and begin Theme 1 again. A song *session* (that is, continuous singing) can last hours.

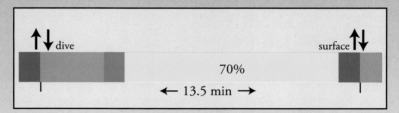

Here the themes (composed as above) are given different colors. All singers in the population follow the same pattern of theme composition and progression. Even the amount of time spent on one theme is similar. During this period (Jan. 2005), about 70 percent of the Hawaii song consisted of Theme 3 (yellow).

Sound spectrographs of the phrases in each theme follow.

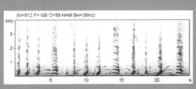

Theme 1

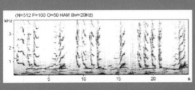

Theme 2

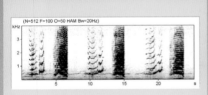

Theme 3

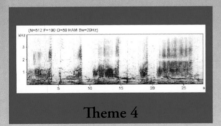

Theme 4

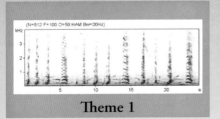

Theme 1

Unique Characteristics

The humpback song is unique in that it gradually changes in composition as it is being sung. That is, small changes in song units will change phrase composition and, in turn, entire themes. (For example, *aaab aaab* in Theme 1 may change to *ab ab*, then eventually drop out altogether.) Yet all the singers in a population sing the same version of the ever-changing song at any one time. Researchers do not know how this is achieved.

Varying Rates of Change

The rate of song change varies — the reason is unknown. Humpback songs studied in Bermuda and Hawaii in the 1970s and 80s changed gradually, with the entire song composition turning over in four or five years. A more recent study in the late 90s off the east coast of Australia showed potential for more rapid change, with the whales there adopting a song from a western Australia population in its entirety over just a two-year period.

To listen to these themes go to
www.whaletrust.org

85

A particularly cooperative whale appears to sing into the hydrophone. He alternated between singing and investigating the boat.

The challenge for researchers is to take the characteristics of the song and add them to our developing picture of singer behavior (that is, the context of singing) and develop a hypothesis on song function.

In summary, the clues to song function are:

- Singing occurs in and around the breeding season.

- Only males are singers.

- Singers sing until joined by other males for brief (usually), non-agonistic interactions then split up, although at times they form pairs or trios.

- Singing and joining are interchangeable behavior patterns, with a single male filling both roles over a period of hours.

- Males may sing when accompanying females, which leads to other males joining (similar to when a female is not present).

- There has been no reliable observation of a female joining a singer (although more subtle interactions not yet documented may be occurring).

- The song is a complex sequence of sounds that progressively changes. Yet all the singers in a population sing essentially the same version at any one time.

Why Do They Sing?

The function of the song has attracted much speculation, but no definitive answer is yet in sight. It has been proposed as a sexual display (to attract mates or signal status to other males), a means of orientation (such as a male spacing mechanism on the breeding grounds or a migratory beacon), a physiological mechanism (to synchronize estrus in females), and even as a type of sonar to locate females. Only a few of these ideas have been investigated beyond the original proposal. Those hypotheses that have received the most attention are discussed below.

Hypothesis 1. **Song is a display by males to attract females and repel males.**

This proposal suggests that the song provides an indication of fitness of the singer and therefore attracts females (as in a lek-type mating system, where males gather to display and females choose among them). In this scenario the song would also be a male spacing mechanism — keeping males separate from each other. There are three major problems with this hypothesis: (1) no evidence that females are attracted to and join singers; (2) males regularly join singers (with brief non-agonistic interactions); and (3) individual differences in song that would likely be the basis for female choice have not been discerned (that is, the songs of all males appear to be the same).

Hypothesis 2. **Song is a display between males to signal status.**

This proposal suggests that the song is part of a dominance-based mating system. The males sort themselves into a hierarchy through displays and fights, and the most dominant animals mate with the most females. In this scenario, the song functions as a display of individual status (thereby maintaining the social order). Research has shown that singing leads to a range of male/male interactions (as would be predicted from this hypothesis). However, in common with a problem facing Hypothesis 1, the differences in song necessary to signal differing male status have not been found. In fact, the opposite is true, as song similarity is a key characteristic. In addition, the rapid

A singer in a classic singing posture just beneath the surface: motionless with nose down and tail up.

changes in song composition are not consistent with the notion of typical mammalian displays of individual status (e.g. antlers).

Hypothesis 3. **Song is a measure of association between males.**

This proposal suggests that the changing nature of the song (with all singers in a region singing the same version at any one time) provides a measure of geographic association between males and a means of organizing male relationships in the breeding season. In turn, this may govern male cooperative or competitive interactions when around females. This hypothesis does, at least, account for both song characteristics and known singer behavior. It arose when it became apparent that the existing hypotheses above did not account for all the observations. However, it must be tested to determine its validity.

MEAGAN JONES

Pulses of Whale Action

There is a flow to behavior in Hawaii. Anyone watching from a boat or shore will notice periods of little surface activity interspersed with bursts of whale action.

The quiet times reflect calmer behavior involving a lone male, two males, or a male/female pair. Surface activity increases when an additional male joins a male escorting a female. The escort defends its position and attempts to chase the challenger away. This often attracts yet more males, leading to one female with multiple, competitive males racing around for hours and miles.

Eventually, the group dissolves, with the peripheral males transitioning into lone behavior such as singing or traveling, and the female with one male escort returning to a resting mode.

Commonly, males sing until joined by another (non-singing) adult male. These interactions are usually brief (minutes) and sociable, involving a few underwater criss-crosses, as shown above, and close parallel surfacings. Then the two generally part, heading in different directions.

Males Joining Singers

The most common interaction of singers, by far, is when a lone (non-singing) adult male joins them. Singing usually (but not always) stops with the joining. The interactions between singer and joiner vary from just a close approach and departure (or drive-by), with the two never surfacing together, to a brief simultaneous surfacing within a whale's length of each other before separation, to longer interactions that include tail lobs, tail throws, breaches, and flippering by one or both whales *(see Actions and Postures, page 210).*

Most of these singer-joiner interactions last less than ten minutes and many, just two or three minutes. In some (approximately one in five), the males do not split up immediately, leading to formation of a pair or, with subsequent joining of other males, a larger group. This variability in interactions of singers and joiners suggests a range of social relationships between the males (which the song apparently mediates).

Recent research has shown that singer-joiner interactions such as these are often just one of a chain across the breeding grounds. That is, once the two males (singer and joiner) have split up, one or both swim directly to other nearby singers, join and split, then move on to the next singer, and so on. This behavior certainly serves to connect males throughout the area, but its specific function (in terms of mating strategy) remains unknown.

Over a four-hour period and a distance of 13 km, the singer was joined, stopped singing, then itself joined and split from two other singers, then it began singing again.

Darling et al.
2006

JIM DARLNG

Joiners

The blows of a single whale are usually sighted several hundred yards from a singer.

The potential joiner may stay at a distance for several surfacings, its dive-times roughly coinciding with the singer's. Some joiners seem to skulk in towards the singer, with two or three blows, a dive below the surface, and so on. Sometimes they decide not to join, with the next blows farther and farther away.

At times there is no hint of a joiner until a 30-ton torpedo zooms in on the singer. At other times one sees nothing, but the song stops and a few seconds later the ex-singer and ex-joiner are sighted moving away in opposite directions. An interaction occurs without researchers being aware of it!

Males Around Females

So far, all the behavior described in this chapter has been between males. Now, as females are added to the picture, it becomes a little more complicated. Reciprocal behavior patterns emerge that can be viewed from both male and female perspectives. The description of these patterns will be repeated to some degree in the following chapter from the female point of view.

Accompanying a Female

A common adult male behavior pattern on the breeding grounds is to pair with a female. This male role is most obvious when the female

It should be obvious who the male escort is in this threesome. Escorts can be downright ornery, expending a lot of energy on bluster and intimidation. At times it is not clear what is aimed at the female and what is aimed at intruders.

has a calf, thereby forming the easily recognizable mother, calf, and escort group. However, a male may also escort a female that does not have a calf, and all that is apparent to the casual observer is a pair of adults. Due to the different stages in the female reproductive cycle (with and without a calf), one might expect a corresponding difference in the male companion behavior or role. But, if it exists, it has yet to be discerned.

86% of mothers with a calf encountered were accompanied by an escort.

Glockner-Ferrari and Ferrari
1985

The escort, stationed below a resting female, will defend his position against male intruders.

It may be that the escort affiliates with a mother long enough to (i) detect if ovulating postpartum and if so remain, (ii) detect if non-ovulating and if so move on, or (iii) detect if mated, and perhaps an additional attempt made. Escort presence could also involve post-copulatory "guarding" behavior.

Mobley and Herman 1985

The behavior of both male/female and male/female/calf groups when not interacting with, or avoiding, other males is often calm, with the animals stationary and resting. In these situations, the adults typically dive for 10–20 minutes, surface for three or four breaths, and then dive again. Some years ago researchers began to call such male/female pairs without a calf "breath-holders," indicating that from the researchers' point of view this is about all they did (this term has stuck). The only obvious difference between these two male/female group types is the calf.

The escort male generally shadows the female. If she is settled and resting, so is the escort. If she is traveling, the escort is usually within a whale's length of her. The escort's breathing and dive patterns generally follow those of the female. In a typical resting situation where the female is motionless, the escort will position himself just off to one side or below, also motionless. Escorts occasionally sing, but most often are quiet. A singing escort may interrupt his normal singing-breathing rhythm in order to follow the female, emphasizing his awareness of her location and behavior.

These male/female pairs are commonly joined by other male(s), upon which the escort usually (but not always) becomes markedly agitated. This involves a range of aggressive behavior from the escort, such as charging the intruder with bubbles streaming from its blowhole, in apparent attempts (some successful, some not) to chase the joining male away. Generally the female (and calf if present) moves away during this male/male interaction. The two males keep pace with the female and often other males in the vicinity rush in to join, thus forming the typical surface active or competitive group described in the next section. The escort (often termed the principal escort when several males are present) may be displaced by another male, or may manage to maintain his position.

JIM DARLING

Warning

The occasional escort will object to a research boat too close (in his view) to 'his' female (even though the boat may be quite a distance away) and has several ways of communicating this. Here, the escort slowly raised his tail up the side and above the 16-foot boat and held it there for enough time to deliver the message.

What, Then, Is the Role of the Escort?

It is clear the escort defends, with substantial aggressiveness, his role of accompanying a female. (In fact, some of these escorts don't really differentiate between challenging whales, small research boats, or underwater observers!) However, his reasons for escorting are not entirely understood.

Actually, some of the very first reports in the 1970s assumed the escort was a female and played an allomaternal (assistant mother) role in protecting the calf. At first glance, this seemed to make sense. Even after the determination that escorts were males, there was speculation that they played a protective role towards mother and calf. This was partially due to a 1950s description of a humpback whale escort 'defending' a mother and calf in conflict with killer whales. That is, some observers interpreted the typical wariness of escorts to intruders, both whale and human alike, as protective of the mother and calf.

However, other researchers suggested the escort is primarily interested in mating rather than protecting the female (and calf). One report noted a mother that had a calf in four consecutive years was accompanied by an escort on each of seven sightings during that period. Another report suggested the duration of the escort/female affiliation may extend beyond courtship and mating if the male engages in post-mating 'guarding' behavior against other males.

The explanation of the escort may be a mixture of the above. The female tolerates the male since it may provide protection against harassment from other males, with the pay-off from the male's view that he will be nearest when she comes into estrus and is receptive to mating.

Competition for Access to Females

Surface active or competitive groups are the most striking humpback behavior on the breeding grounds, characterized by fast-traveling whales and high-energy activity. They can often be seen from miles away as three, four, ten or more blows shoot up in quick succession as the action moves across the horizon at high speed. These groups are composed of multiple males competing for access to a female, presumably in estrus. It is not known if mating occurs during this action, but it seems a possibility as extended penes and close rolling and

When several males follow a female the action is complex. There is competition, with the escort (or principal escort) nearest the female fiercely taking on all challengers, and at the same time there may be cooperation between pairs or even trios of males to outmaneuver him.

contact have been observed. On the other hand, the movement is often so rapid, some doubt mating could occur.

Competitive groups are typically composed of one female with or without a calf (termed the nuclear animal by some authors), usually in the lead, but at times in the center, of multiple males. (There are several reported cases of two females present with multiple males, but these are exceptional.)

This group moves rapidly about the area 'picking up' additional males and 'losing' other males in the process. The principal escort (nearest the female) is invariably the most agitated and active, clearly defending his position with exuberant lunges and bubblestreams, high-speed chases, and blocks of incoming whales. These groups are characterized by bursts of speed (10 knots and more) and changes in direction as the secondary escorts (or challengers) apparently attempt to outmaneuver the

This competition (amongst males) involves fluke thrashes, the blowing of bubblestreams and physical contact, some of which appears designed to hurt an opponent — bleeding wounds are seen on the competing escorts.

Tyack and Whitehead 1983

97

Threats and Full-On Brawls

Male humpback whales threaten and fight with each other, mostly over access to a female. This behavior ranges from threat displays to fierce physical contact.

Threats include bubblestreaming, underwater blows, a posture with back arched and head above the surface (head lift), gulping air at the surface (resulting in impressively extended throat pleats) and then explosively releasing the air underwater, lunging and/or slapping the chin on the surface, clapping the jaws open and shut, and directing a tail lash at another animal without hitting it *(see Actions and Postures)*.

These displays can shift into physical contact involving blocking and chasing, which may include tail lashes (even slapping another male's head with the flukes), rear body throws, and collisions. The whale's weapons are its tail, whole body and, at times, its head. The combatants may receive minor wounds such as bloody head knobs, dorsal fins, and tail stocks. Many of the scars and scratches that decorate some whales, particularly males, result from these encounters.

JIM DARLING

JIM DARLING

FLIP NICKLIN © National Geographic Society reprinted with permission

principal escort. Most of the interaction occurs between the principal escort and one or two of the challengers, with other animals following along on the periphery. Occasionally the secondary escorts replace the principal escort, but most often they just leave the group after a period ranging from minutes to many hours.

Social Sounds

The whales in competitive groups may make a wide range of loud, energetic, underwater sounds ranging from whistles and screeches to grunts and growls, collectively referred to as "social sounds." These sounds are a 'force' on the breeding grounds as, on hearing them, males will frequently interrupt other activity, such as singing, and rapidly travel for miles to join the group.

To date there is only one study that has specifically investigated social sounds. This work involved spending months in Hawaii maneuvering well in front of competitive groups and recording them as they passed by, then correlating sounds with observations of the groups themselves.

The study found social sounds:

- Occurred almost exclusively in groups containing three or more whales and were rarely heard near single whales, pairs, or mother/calf groups.

- Increased dramatically in number when a new whale entered a group.

- Increased in number with group size, suggesting that each group member contributed to overall sound production.

- Could be overlapping, that is, from two or more whales vocalizing simultaneously. (This led to speculation that competing males produce the sounds, possibly as threat gestures.)

- Could be rare in some large groups that showed little surface activity.

During these multiple male/single female competitive interactions, a wide range of loud sounds — including groans, hiccups, whistles, screams, and thrums — are emitted by the males.

This researcher speculated that social sounds act to demonstrate aggression or agitation as adult males compete for temporary social dominance within the group and thereby closeness to the female.

Humpbacks appear to sense and respond to large groups of whales up to at least nine km (over five miles) away. Acoustic cues are likely candidates.

**Tyack and Whitehead
1983**

Five males are following a mother, calf, and escort. The question of how the five relate to each other is open — that is, do some or all coordinate in some way to try to dislodge the escort?

Observations of pairs of males acting as a non-competitive unit against other males, or attempting to corral a female by one chasing and the other blocking, suggest some level of cooperation.

Cooperation for Access to a Female

In contrast to male competition on the breeding grounds, there are suggestions of cooperative behavior among some males to gain access to a female. This may include the formation of male coalitions that work together and against other males in competitive situations, or possibly in attempts to constrain the movements of a female.

The idea of male pairs or coalitions working together or cooperating against other males in competitive groups first arose from observations on the West Indies humpback whale breeding grounds. As early as the 1980s, when male competitive behavior was first being described, one researcher noted male pairs working as cooperative units within competitive groups.

Similar observations from this and other breeding areas have appeared sporadically in the literature ever since. For example, in the mid-1990s,

Australian researchers noted a male pair that moved between competitive groups and engaged in agonistic displays with other animals, but not with each other. They speculated that, if subordinate animals join competitive groups together rather than alone, the odds of one of them outmaneuvering the dominant males, and subsequently mating, may increase.

There are also a few observations of a team of two males seemingly cooperating to corral a female. The most complete of these to date, from Hawaii, involved a singer and joiner that formed a pair and immediately approached a nearby mother with calf. The ex-singer, bubblestreaming, chased the female, while the ex-joiner appeared to block by repeatedly crossing directly in front of her.

This possible connection between singing, joining, and male cooperation raises interesting questions about the function of the song. A further hint at this potential link is an observation of a singer being joined, then another male joining this pair to form a trio that immediately swam together to a passing competitive group. However, clear observations connecting singers and joiners with cooperative behavior around a female are few and far between. Therefore, the questions of if, and how, these behavior patterns may be connected, although very intriguing, are far from answered.

The possibility that males form coalitions cannot be dismissed. That is, humpback males may cooperate in their effort to secure access to a female.

Clapham et al. 1992

Most male/male associations were characterized by non-agonistic and occasionally cooperative interactions.

Brown and Corkeron 1995

The pair (singer and joiner) were joined by a third male and the trio rushed to a passing competitive group as a unit.

Darling and Bérubé 2001

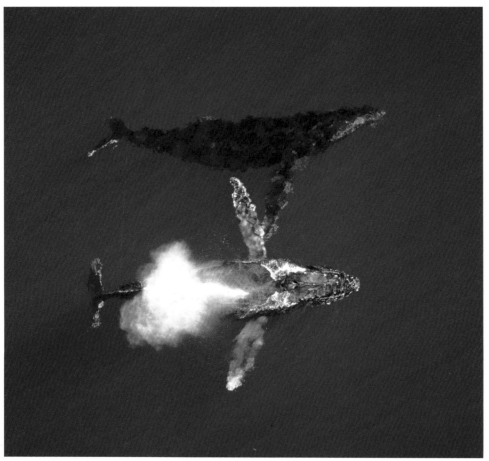

Potential cooperation in mating situations and the apparent care (or guarding) of an associate that died in a competitive group hint that humpback males may have more complex relationships than initially considered.

Males Caring for Other Males?

One of the more unusual observations of humpback male behavior occurred on February 9, 1996 in waters off Lahaina, Maui. A whale-watching boat reported a whale had died in a competitive group, and researchers rushed to the scene. (This is the only documented case of a humpback whale dying in the midst of a competitive group.) The dead whale was a male. Another adult male remained beside the dead whale for over four hours, alternating between clasping it with its flippers or stationing itself beside or below, and on several occasions placed himself between the dead whale and a diver filming, directing tail lashes and other threat gestures at the diver.

One of several possible explanations of this behavior was that it was a form of helping (epimeletic) behavior between males. There are reports from whaling ships of adult humpbacks standing by or supporting those injured or killed by harpoons. If this was the explanation for the behavior, it seems more reflective of extended associations and cooperation between some individual males rather than universal competition, as has often been presumed.

The interpretation of the behaviors of the live whales toward the dead whale remains problematic but may offer a new perspective on social relations among male humpbacks on the winter grounds.

Pack et al.
1998

Mature males travel to the breeding grounds to mate with as many females as possible. All male behavior — the singing, joining singers, escorting a female, and competing, individually or in cooperative coalitions — is related to this one objective. Researchers have described many male behavior patterns relatively well (compared to female patterns) over the last thirty years. However, we do not yet understand how all these patterns are 'connected' to each other or, for many, what their specific function is within the mating system.

107

Mating — The Male Perspective

Quick Info

What do males do in Hawaii?

Adult male humpback whales look for receptive females, pair with them, and attempt to defend that position against challengers, or they challenge existing escorts for access to a female.

What is humpback whale song, who sings, why?

Humpback whale song is a complex series of sounds, typically ten to fifteen minutes long, repeated over and over by adult males during the breeding season. The song gradually changes as it is being sung, yet all singers sing essentially the same version at any one time. The function of the song is not known.

What follows singing?

Singers most often sing until joined by non-singing adult males. The interaction typically lasts just a few minutes and is rarely aggressive, then the pair usually splits and heads in different directions.

What is an escort?

Escort is the term given an adult male that accompanies a female. It is most often used in cases where the female has a calf, but similar behavior occurs when the female is without a calf. The escort defends his position with the female from other males.

What is a surface active group?

A surface active or competitive group (interchangeable terms) is composed of a single female, presumably in or near estrus, and multiple males competing for access to her. A principal escort, nearest the female, is most active in defending his position against the challengers.

Do males fight with each other?

Yes, males fight. These events range from threats where there is no physical clash to all-out collisions and blows. Males fight when competing with each other around a female in estrus.

What are social sounds?

Social sounds are a wide variety of sounds including whistles, screeches, grunts, and growls made by males in competitive groups. They might be threats.

Do males cooperate with each other?

At times, males apparently cooperate to corral (or otherwise gain access to) a female in estrus. They may form cooperative pairs that work together and against other males in competitive situations.

Chapter 5

Mating — The Female Perspective

By traveling to Hawaii, female humpback whales make themselves accessible to sexually active males — a bunch of them. If mating is not an objective, they are definitely in the wrong place. But what happens between a female and the males? What forces are at work? The interactions that occur between her arrival and departure a few weeks later, newly pregnant, are unexplored (scientific) territory.

If a humpback male's biggest challenge in mating is simply finding a female in estrus, a female's may be to mate successfully with a high-quality (fit, healthy) male with the least possible energy expenditure. In other words, the female may want to be picky, but not so picky the energetic cost is higher than the value of the male upgrade. The intriguing question for researchers is, how does she achieve this? Does she simply swim onto the breeding grounds and make herself available? Does she behave in a way that encourages male competition? Does she more actively choose males with specific attributes?

Knowledge of female humpback behavior in a mating context may be the least-known aspect of this species' behavior. This chapter explores what we do know regarding the female perspective, describes some possible but unproven scenarios, and shows that researchers have more questions than answers.

Pairing With, Avoiding, And (Perhaps) Choosing Males

The female whale in Hawaii is almost always (either by choice or coercion) accompanied by one or more males. She may be calmly accompanied by a single adult male or pursued by several competitive males. In the latter case, she is eventually left with one male companion, which may or may not be her original escort. There is little doubt that a female does not always seek this male attention and at times tries to discourage or escape it. (This may be the reason for cooperative male behavior, as it is much harder to escape two males than one.) The ultimate question here is whether a female chooses, either passively or actively, specific males over others.

When on the breeding grounds and therefore fasting, females may behave: (1) to accomplish mating while spending the least amount of time (for overall energetic considerations); (2) to maximize the number of males and minimize the number of females encountered.

Gabriele
1992

Female behavior is as subtle as male behavior is overt. They often seem to be doing very little, lying absolutely still in the water — but in any larger view, they are probably orchestrating much of the male behavior around them.

A portion of the female humpback whales that migrate to Hawaii are present only to mate — having recently weaned a yearling or completed a non-reproductive year. (That is, they are not in late pregnancy or with newborn.) They are often found paired with a male.

Female Roles

Overall, female behavior patterns in Hawaii fall into two realms: mating and then birth and newborn care. Intuitively, these should be quite separate, even mutually exclusive, but it's not entirely clear that this is the case.

Mature females that come to Hawaii are either:

- Not pregnant, having just completed a year of child-care and recently weaned a yearling (which may still be present or nearby), or having completed a non-reproductive year.

- In late pregnancy and about to give birth (or with a brand-new calf presumably born en route).

For the first category of females, the objective is to mate, then return to the feeding grounds. For the second category, while the primary objective is presumably birth, protection of the newborn, and preparation of the calf for return to the feeding grounds *(see Chapter 3)*, these new mothers undergo estrus and are also involved in mating activity.

Successful mating may involve maximizing contact with males, as this would seem the best way to accomplish the objective. In contrast, successful birth and newborn care may involve minimizing contact with rowdy males to conserve energy and protect the calf. This seems to make sense. However, we find all females, whether or not they have a newborn tagging along, involved in similar (presumably mating-related) behavior.

There are several possible explanations for this conduct. (1) Perhaps the energetic mating activity does not impact the newborn and it is not critical for new mothers to minimize contact with males and/or the value of the potential pregnancy is great enough to risk the newborn. (2) Male interaction with mothers is solely harassment and coercion, near impossible to avoid, and not a female reproductive strategy. (3) There are in fact differences in how single females, and mothers with a calf, interact with males, but they have not yet been discerned.

These questions aside, following is a very basic approach to female humpback behavior in Hawaii: what we see females do, and what we don't see females do.

Many female humpbacks arrive in Hawaii in late pregnancy and are present to give birth and/or to nurture newborn. However, with calf alongside, they may also be involved in mating activity, often escorted by one or more males.

What We See

On any day of the winter, where are the females and what are they doing? The answer to these questions changes somewhat over the season. To start, the proportion of females without a calf versus females with a calf reverses itself as the season progresses. That is, from December to February, a female is more likely to be seen without a calf, but from February through April is far more likely to be found with a calf. However, apart from newborn care, female behavior appears similar whether she is a current mother or not.

The three social situations in which a female (with and without a calf) is encountered are:

Female with an Adult Male

A female is often found paired with an adult male. In the second half of the season, as mentioned above, most females in an adult pair also have a calf in tow.

The female in these social units is often stationary, apparently resting. This suggests she accepts or at least tolerates the male companion. However, on occasion the female is obviously fleeing, suggesting that the presence of males (or at least some males) is not always acceptable.

Female with Multiple Males

Throughout the winter season, females are found in front of, or otherwise the focus of, multiple males in competitive groups. The females are either being chased by, or are leading, the competitive males. Competitive groups occur around females without a calf and females with a calf, probably indicating she is in or near estrus in both cases.

Female Discouraging Males

Female humpbacks at times behave in ways that make it quite clear they would prefer that the attentive males get lost. In scientific terms, the females appear to influence selection of mates in several overt ways. Our understanding of this behavior is thin, but there is little doubt it occurs.

At times, females accept the presence of males; at other times (*as shown above*), the female flees, clearly trying to lose the unwanted company.

For example, it is apparent a female may avoid unwanted mating by raising her fluke, tail stock, and genital region vertically above the surface of the water and out of reach of males. The problem with this maneuver (for the female) is it means her head is underwater and eventually she has to breathe. There are also observations of females behaving aggressively towards sub-adult males, a social group that may be pests at mating time. Other examples of females discouraging or avoiding males include leading males into shallows, or to boats, where they seem to 'rub them off' and lose them.

Current descriptions of this behavior are based on just a few observations and it clearly deserves further study. What is not known is whether this 'discouragement' occurs only when the female is avoiding all males or just certain males. The latter possibility may be evidence of deliberate female choice of mates. In other words, these observations could be just the tip of the iceberg of female mating strategy.

On seven occasions (in Hawaii) a female led males repeatedly towards vessels, or the shoreline, resulting in either the replacement of an escort, or the retreat of the pursuing males.

Glockner-Ferrari and Ferrari
1985

A nuclear animal (that is, a female) that does not wish to be courted may lead the surface active group into areas where coral heads are abundant (on Silver Bank in the Caribbean) in an effort to shake off aggressive males.

Mattila et al.
1989

117

This photograph shows a mature female humpback not accompanied by any males. This is a fairly uncommon occurrence on the breeding grounds, even for mothers with newborn calves.

What We Don't (Or Rarely) See

Females Are Rarely Alone

An adult female is not often found alone on the breeding grounds. This claim comes from studies that analyzed multiple sightings of known (photo-identified) individual females and the social situation they were seen in on each sighting — females were almost always accompanied by males.

Another way of approaching this subject is to look at females whose sex is, in fact, determined at a glance — those with a calf. The proportion of mothers with an escort is consistently (from several studies) around 85 percent, meaning only three out of twenty are without a male companion. If this ratio can be applied to females without a calf (and it is not at all clear it can be, as one expects current mothers may not encourage males as much as potential mothers), it means some females are finding time alone without males or babies. But remember, females whose priority is pregnancy are not being successful if they are alone.

Females Do Not Associate with Other Females

Female/female interactions and associations on the breeding grounds are very rare (in complete contrast to male/male ones). The handful of observations (in over thirty years) of two females in the same group suggests it is accidental (such as when two competitive groups run into each other by chance) and remedied quickly. In fact, mothers with a calf often actively avoid each other, altering course to increase the distance from other such pairs. Curiously, in other baleen species such as gray whales, the females do not seem to avoid each other. Moreover, on the feeding grounds, humpback females associate freely in groups.

Females Do Not Join Singers

Females are not seen approaching or joining male singers, although males escorting a female sometimes sing. In one study in Hawaii, the sex of whales that joined singers was determined genetically (through collection of skin biopsies), and none was a female. This finding has been supported with similar studies on other humpback whale breeding grounds.

In 27 repeat sightings of females without a calf, all were accompanied by males on each sighting. Mothers with calves were accompanied by a male in 102 of 123 observations (83%).

Darling
1983

JIM DARLING

Copulation?

Copulation has not been observed — therefore, it is only a presumption that females identified in pairs and multiple male groups are involved in mating behavior.

The following observations within pairs or larger groups of adults suggest mating or attempted mating:

- Females followed or chased by males.
- 'Nosing' of genital area by males, possibly checking for estrus.
- Excited rolling and flippering in close proximity or contact with other whales.
- Female tail arching, or contorting of the tail stock into an "S" shape, suggesting presentation of the genital area.
- Female rolling, or extending tail out of the water, to put her genital area above the surface, suggesting avoidance.
- Extended penes.

119

Mating Situations

When does mating occur and in what groups? One approach to this question is to take sightings of females with tiny babies and rewind history 11–12 months, which should lead us to the time of mating situations. Multi-year studies based on the identification of individual animals allow us to do this. All the repeat sightings of an individual female (sex determined by presence of a calf in one of the sightings) over a series of years are analyzed, and in some cases a female that gave birth one year had also been seen the previous year involved in other behavior. So we connect the two. There is no guarantee that this exercise establishes when mating occurs, but at this point it is all we have to work with.

Pairs of adult whales, surfacing and diving together, are a common sight in the early winter season in Hawaii. One is a female, the other a male.

Collective research efforts have provided a number of examples of females observed with single males or in multiple male groups during one winter, then re-identified with a calf the following winter. This is also true of females that gave birth in successive years. These observations, combined with the understood gestation period of 11–12 months, indicate the possibility that mating occurred in the pair or multiple-male group. Specific examples are provided in the following plate.

In the previous chapter we described the two social situations or groups that include both males and a female from the former's perspective. We review them here, but from the female viewpoint.

Rewinding History: When Does Mating Occur?

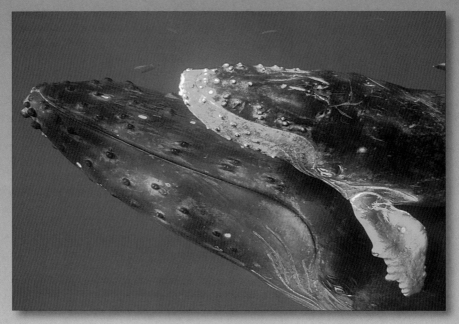

One way of estimating when and where mating occurs is to look at what a female was doing 11 to 12 months (gestation period) prior to being sighted with a new calf. Long-term photo-identification studies allow this re-winding of history. Specific examples follow.

Female in a Pair

Example 1 A female (#13) identified as one of a pair (Mar. 3, 1980) had a calf the following season. The other member of the pair on this date was not sexed, but had been seen in a group of 5–7 adults earlier in the day, suggesting it was a male. This pair was milling, with significant surface activity including flippering, breaching, rolling belly up, and one animal swimming upside down close to the surface just prior to blowing.

Example 2 A female (#17) was identified twice in a pair with different partners (Jan. 30 and Feb. 18, 1980) a year before she was seen with a calf. On January 30 her partner was a known male. The only behavior noted was that the male lifted his head above the water when he was swimming beside the female. He had a raw, bloody area on his peduncle, probably the result of fighting with other males over access to the female.

Female in a Larger Group (of males)

Example 1 This female (#15) had been identified in a group of four or more adults a year (Feb. 18, 1980) before she was identified with a calf (Feb. 15, 1981). The behavior of this larger group included flippering and rolling, along with a variety of apparently aggressive interactions including head lifts, chin slaps, jaw claps, tail lashes, and bubblestreams. Specific behavior patterns were not correlated with individuals.

Example 2 A female (#18) was identified in large groups (Feb. 1 and 6, 1980) a year before she was found with a calf. On February 1 she was seen with a group of four or more adults and later in a group of eight or more adults. The behavior patterns noted were flippering, head lifts, jaw claps, tail lobs, and underwater blows. This example also indicates that a female may be close enough to estrus over a period of six days to attract males.

It is important to emphasize that the inferences made here are just that — they are the best guesses with the information we have. The unanswered questions of when, where, and with whom successful mating occurs are a source of continued frustration to researchers. Clearly, the answers are fundamental to understanding behavior on the breeding grounds, but to date they have been elusive.

Female/male pairs often
appear synchronized in their
underwater movements.

Female/Male Pair

Female/male pairs are relatively stable (in comparison to larger groups or male pairs), often maintaining a calm, exclusive union for hours to a day or longer. Instances of conclusive sexing of both individuals (when a calf is not present) combined with extended behavioral observations are limited, although studies addressing this are underway. General patterns that are likely female/male follow below.

Often the female/male pair is stationary, except when surfacing. They make near-synchronized long dives of 20–30 minutes or more. Underwater observations indicate these pairs dive to approximately 50–100 feet (15–30 m) and stop. (As mentioned before, these long dives have caused this behavior to be dubbed "breath-holding.")

Typically one whale is in a horizontal position, and the other in a more vertical, head-down position. Beyond this, there is little obvious interaction or activity between the whales (this calmness is at times interrupted with brief bouts of rolling, flippering, or breaching by one or both animals). Occasionally, the male has been observed singing, although this is an exception rather than the rule.

The development or instigation of these pairs is not understood, but outwardly they are (at least temporarily) mutually acceptable as there is no obvious escape behavior by the female.

Eight females were seen as one of a pair of adults or in large groups of adults in the years they were not identified with a calf. Two mothers that gave birth in consecutive years were accompanied by either a single escort or multiple males in the year before the consecutive birth.

Darling
1983

In 13 of 16 cases where females with a calf had also been seen the previous season, they were in a pair.

Gabriele
1992

The most likely explanations are that a female is approaching estrus and accepting of the male attention, or alternatively, having mated, she is allowing a guard against unwanted attention.

As discussed earlier *(see Chapter 4)*, these pairs tend to persist until another adult (male) joins, potentially leading to the formation of a larger competitive group. The pair may re-form after the larger group breaks up.

Females Leading Multiple Males

Adult females with or without a calf can be followed by groups of males (anywhere from two to twenty), with all the attendant aggressive activity described in the previous chapter. The big question here is, are these females victims of male harassment and coercion, or are they the instigators and beneficiaries of the male competition? We don't know and, of course, it could be either in different situations.

JIM DARLING

One scenario is that the competitive groups are ultimately a test of male fitness, with the most 'fit' (strongest, smartest) gaining access to the female. In this case, the female, by moving rapidly in front of the group and leading it over substantial distances, both avoids unwanted mating and attracts as many males as possible, thereby increasing the level of competition in the group and ultimately gaining a preferable mate.

The other possibility is that the female does not want to be hounded by a bunch of males. It has been speculated that a female may tolerate a single male escort solely because he may discourage the attention of other males and reduce this harassment. This seems to make sense for mothers with a small calf, where the energy expenditure used in fleeing from males could be an impediment to the calf's survival.

Mating may occur in the midst of surface active groups, but it has not been documented. Commotion on the surface like this is often seen, but it's usually not clear if the female is in the middle somewhere or if it's all competing males.

Do Females Choose Their Mates Based On Their Song?

The idea that females may select mates based on listening to their songs is undoubtedly the best-known unproven hypothesis regarding the breeding behavior of humpbacks. This view has received a great deal of attention in twenty-five or so years of scientific and popular publications, yet there exists no evidence for it. There are very few actual observations of females joining singers, song playback experiments have failed to attract females, and there are strong indications that the song is primarily a signal between males.

Advocates of the "female choice of mate by song" view, in acknowledgment of the lack of observations of females actually joining singers, have proposed an alternative scenario still based on female choice. They speculate that a female need not approach a singer, but instead provide an 'invitation' for the male to approach her. This idea suggests a female may indicate her preference for a particular singer and hence song by whether she allows the pursuing singer to join her, or perhaps with a return vocalization (that has not been heard nor listened for). In this view, the song may not serve to bring females directly to the singer, but may still serve as a basis for female selection.

Another suggestion is that the song may simply allow a female to locate and evaluate singers, and she may lead a competitive group towards the loudest, deepest song she hears, inviting the singer to compete. It is important to note that these possibilities have not been investigated, or even observed.

We are just beginning to understand the mating behavior of female humpback whales. In contrast to the overt singing and fighting of males, female behavior is often subtle — so much so that it tempts the impression they are doing very little. In fact, though, it is probable the females are instigating and even 'managing' much of the behavior we see. There is much yet to be revealed and there are compelling questions for researchers who wish to explore the behavior of female humpback whales.

Although a common notion, there is no evidence females choose males based on their song.

Mating — The Female Perspective

Quick Info

What do female humpbacks do in Hawaii?

Females come to Hawaii to either mate or to give birth. Some do both in the same season. Estrus females need to associate with males, whereas birthing females do not (and their behavior may vary accordingly).

Who are females with?

On the breeding grounds, we see females accompanied by a single male (that is, in a pair) and in larger surface active groups where she is chased by (or leads) multiple males. Adult females are rarely alone on the breeding grounds.

Do females associate with each other?

Female humpback whales do not purposely associate with, and seem to actively avoid, each other on the breeding grounds. Groups with more than one female have been observed, but these are short-lived and appear to occur by chance.

When does mating occur?

Mating has not been documented. However, there are examples of individual females identified on the breeding grounds about a year before being seen with a calf. At that time they were either one of a pair or the focus of a competitive group. The odds are mating occurs in these situations.

What is the female mating strategy?

We do not know. The question is whether or not females simply move onto the breeding grounds and let the males compete — with, in theory, the strongest or fittest male winning access — or whether they select mates in a more specific way.

Do females choose their mate by listening to his song?

There is no evidence that this occurs, but the idea persists.

Chapter 6

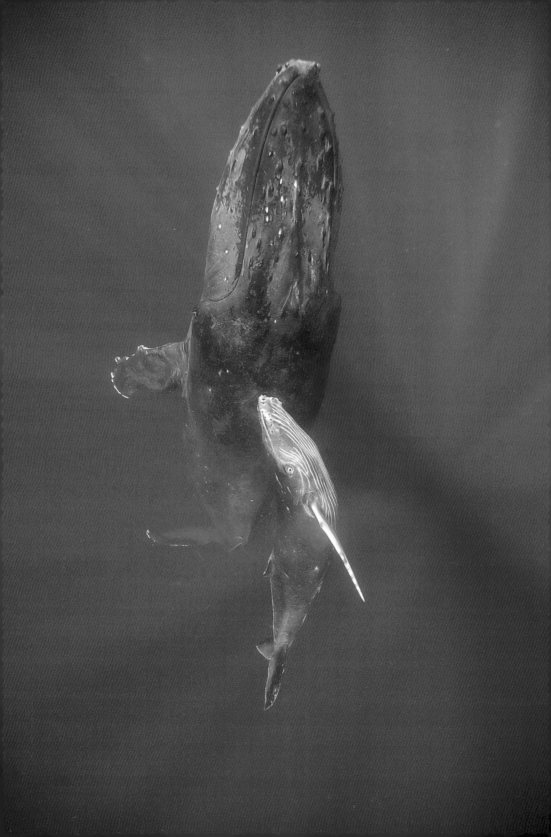

Newborns and Juveniles

Through the eventual synchrony of a female's receptivity and a male's persistence, a pregnancy results. The mother-to-be then heads for summer feeding grounds to fuel for a successful gestation and healthy baby. The following winter, near term (or as a new mother), she again passes through the channels of the Hawaiian Islands. This chapter picks up the story here.

Birth is not easily (actually, so far never) documented. Our earliest glimpse of a newborn humpback is generally when a tiny light-colored, wrinkled, bent-dorsal-finned creature puffs alongside its relatively massive mother. The nearshore habitat new mothers seek out makes them the closest whales to human activity. Calves spend their first weeks traveling, resting, nursing, and playing. Then they accompany their mothers across the North Pacific to distant feeding grounds.

A year after birth, the young animals migrate to Hawaii with their mothers. Some break the maternal bond en route, others on the breeding grounds. Consequently, there is a significant youth culture in Hawaiian waters comprising these yearlings and older juveniles that have not yet reached sexual maturity. These young whales are often on the periphery of adult activity, mimicking their behavior and interacting with mature males.

Maternal Priorities

Since the birth of a humpback whale has not been documented, the specific behavior patterns of the mother immediately before, during, and after birth are not known. It is likely the mother's behavior is geared towards rest, nursing, and protection of the young. The last of these endeavors may have three fronts: (1) avoiding, or at least controlling, interactions with sexually active males; (2) avoiding interactions with other mothers with a calf; and (3) guarding against potential predators.

Those Persistent Males

The need for separation of mother and newborn from the male harassment surrounding mating activity (at least at critical times) may be a major driving force of mother/young behavior in Hawaii. A female's options for accomplishing this separation in the short term include simply dodging the activity—for instance, moving to inshore, shallow waters. In the longer term, seasonal adjustment of birth times may have occurred (birth before reaching Hawaii or at least out of sync with peak mating times). Both of these strategies may be beneficial in terms of health of the newborn.

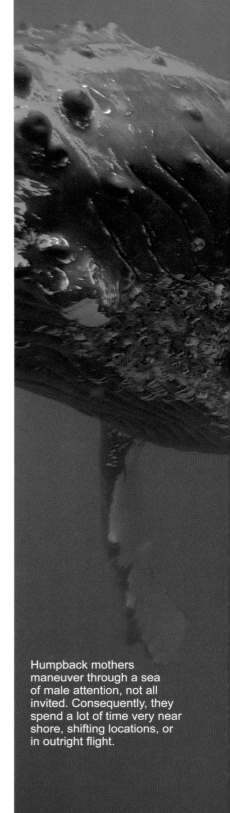

Humpback mothers maneuver through a sea of male attention, not all invited. Consequently, they spend a lot of time very near shore, shifting locations, or in outright flight.

Mothers with newborn calves steer clear of other mothers, moving away to keep their distance.

Avoiding the Neighbors

Mothers with a young calf actively avoid any close association with other mothers with young. This can pose a challenge in peak season when the density of these mother/calf groups can be as high as one every several hundred square yards or so. If a mother and calf are traveling, they must keep changing course; if stationary, they must interrupt rest or nursing and shift locations to avoid interaction.

Several explanations for mother and calf avoidance of other groups have been proposed, including the possibility of such interactions leading to:

- Premature social interactions for the calf
- Increased energy expenditure
- Interruption of nursing bouts
- Mistaken imprinting or nursing attempts
- Separation of calves from mothers
- Injury to calves

However, just to complicate this, remember that females without a calf do not associate either, so perhaps the explanation lies within the broader female reproductive strategy, rather than just how these interactions may impact calves.

The First Weeks

Humpback babies are born into some of the most beautiful water in the world — the warm, glimmering blues of the subtropics. They emerge into an environment saturated with sound, with singing all around them, day and night, through the first weeks of life. They soon learn their boundaries, the surface, the vital interface between water and the air they breathe, which they will try to break through with their antics, and the sea floor when in the shallows with a resting mother.

In their first days, calves experience the warmth and clarity of the sea, the connection to a large community of whales, and no shortage of activity as their mother navigates through encounters with one or many males. They learn about fish that follow them around feeding on bits of skin, dolphins that bow-ride on mom, boats and researchers and, perhaps, predators.

Predators

Little is known about predators on humpback whales in Hawaii. We don't even really know whether predation is a significant problem or whether threats are minimal and this is one reason the mothers-to-be come to Hawaii. There *are* potential predators in Hawaiian waters, including groups of large dolphins called false killer whales *(Pseudorca)*, and pygmy killer whales *(Feresa)* — their names hint at their voraciousness. True killer whales *(Orcinus orca)* are occasionally seen in Hawaiian waters, but are certainly more common (and more of a threat to humpbacks) in cooler seas. Then, of course, there are the ever-present tiger sharks.

Schools of false and pygmy killer whales could be a factor in mother/newborn behavior. Since the 1980s, there have been reports of false killer whales harassing and possibly attacking mothers and newborn calves. One fisherman watched a group of false killer whales attack a calf off the Big Island, leaving substantial blood and a missing calf. It seems that some level of harassment of humpback mothers with a calf by false killer whales is fairly common, but how often this leads to the injury or death of a calf is not known.

Humpback calves, like most young mammals, rely on their mothers for protection.

Tiger sharks are, without any doubt, a major predator in the Hawaiian breeding area, and they are not known for fussiness in what they eat. There have been several observations of them gorging on dead whales, following sick calves, and even attacking living but injured sub-adults. However, whether they actively or successfully pursue healthy calves is not known.

Options for predator avoidance in the ocean are limited. Shallow water is apparently key to one successful strategy. The shallows reduce the number of directions to guard by eliminating attacks from below and above. They may also confound the echolocation and communication abilities of predatory whales. This could be the (or at least one) explanation for mother and newborn preference for inshore habitat.

BILL SCOTT

Maternal females may use shallower water to avoid harassment and injury to calves from sexually active males, turbulent offshore conditions or predators.

Smultea
1994

Safe Haven?

The level of predation on newborn whales in Hawaiian waters may be low compared to other parts of the humpbacks' range.

However, there are potential predators, including schools of large black dolphins called false killer whales that, at times, will harass and apparently kill a calf. In the photos above a humpback mother blocks two false killer whales from her calf.

The actual birth of a humpback whale has yet to be documented, but tiny babies such as this one (only days or even hours old) are often encountered.

A Birth — Who Will See It First?

A most striking non-observation in Hawaii is the birth of a baby humpback whale. With tens of thousands of whale-watch hours each season, as well as the presence of multiple researchers for over thirty years, a birth has not been documented. It's amazing.

To be specific, a birth may well have been seen, and there are one or two reports each winter where the observers have been convinced. However, it is yet to be documented — that is, to date no photographs or scientific observations of the actual delivery exist.

At the same time, there is little question that birth does occur during the winter season in Hawaii. The evidence is this:

- Studies from whaling operations clearly show that term fetuses and birth coincide with winter months.

- In Hawaii, observations of tiny calves with folded dorsal fins and crease marks (clearly within days if not hours of birth) are common.

- A humpback whale placenta (mammalian organ that nourishes the fetus) was found in Hawaii shortly after a very young calf appeared beside an adult.

- One study reported a sighting of a photo-identified female without a calf on January 31 (1981) and with a calf seventeen days later on February 16 (1981), indicating a birth had occurred.

On January 11, 1994, an extremely active adult dove for eight minutes. Upon resurfacing, a very small calf was noted next to the whale. A large placenta was found (in the vicinity) 15 minutes later.

Silvers and Salden 1997

The fact that it is so difficult to see an actual birth may be an indication of just how critical the separation of birth from the ongoing activity (both whale and human) in the region is. Does it occur before the whales reach the Hawaiian Islands? Does it occur at night?

When Do We See Humpback Calves?

The earliest date of a published sighting of a female with a young calf in Hawaii (at the time of writing) is on December 24. However, this is a case where the common knowledge from whale-watching sightings outweighs the published material and certainly young calves have been reported prior to that date.

Early studies (1980s) in Hawaii suggested mothers with newborn calves were relatively rare before the end of January (just two pairs in five seasons in one comprehensive survey). However, there have been no published reports of comparable information in recent years. Anecdotal information suggests calves are more common in the early season today than they were in the 1980s, but this has not been quantified.

These sightings are not birthdays — whereas some of the calves seen in the early winter in Hawaii are tiny (and clearly recent additions), others are a relatively good size and likely weeks to months old. (One more humpback whale enigma: If the larger calves seen in Hawaii are born en route, what is the reason for migrating to Hawaii?)

After the beginning of February, the number of mothers with calves increases markedly (in fact, they are everywhere), and they are among the last groups present at the very end of the season in May and even June.

A bent-over dorsal fin on a tiny, creased calf (*left*) is a sure sign of a very new addition to Hawaii's humpback population.

JIM DARLING

Large Mammal Babies

Newborn humpback whales are like any baby mammal. They are (whale) cute, endearing, and a little out of control. They alternate between bouts of energetic flipping and flopping around the mother, then resting quietly tucked under her flipper or chin, or riding (slipstreaming) above her mouth. They have challenges with coordination and diving. Sometimes they just can't get down to mom resting 20 feet (7 m) below, and end up flopping back to the surface, floating up tail first. Often the calf will twirl its body and swim upside down.

They are very curious. They have no fear of boats or researchers, with mothers often having to retrieve them from these explorations. However, some mothers see no threat in this and appear to continue sleeping as the calf amuses itself with objects in its environment. More than one researcher has been surprised with a calf's nose pressed up against his/her face mask (and wondering just what the mother is thinking at that point!).

Newborns — How Do They Spend Their First Weeks In Hawaii?

In their first few weeks, newborn hump-back whales travel (a lot) and then they rest, play and, of course, eat.

Travel — The Most Common Activity!

Mothers with a calf circulate through the main Hawaiian Island chain, as do other humpback whale social groups. Day-to-day resightings of a specific mother and her calf in one location are rare. The purpose, or cause, of this steady movement is not known; perhaps it is part of the swimming regimen preparing the calf for migration, or possibly the result of the mother being pursued or harassed by males.

The most common mother and calf activity is moving around their winter range. The reasons for this are not clear, but may include getting away from rowdy males or preparing the calf for migration to feeding grounds.

> *Travel was by far the most common activity of mothers with calves. . . . Rest was the next most common activity, with the proportion of time spent at rest increasing as calves matured.*
>
> **Cartwright**
> **2005**

Resting mother, calf, and escort groups are common. The calf cannot hold its breath as long as adults so must rise to the surface by itself every few minutes, then dive again to its mother's side. Above, a calf rises solo to the surface with its mother below, and escort on guard off to one side.

Resting

Mothers with a young calf are often found resting. Typically, the mother lies in a horizontal position at a depth ranging from approximately 15 to 50 feet (5 to 15 m) below the surface. The calf usually positions itself directly below the mother's chin or tucked under a flipper. The calf needs to breathe at shorter intervals than the mother and therefore must rise to the surface alone every few minutes to blow and inhale three or four times while swimming in a circular pattern above its mom. The calf then dives back down to its mother (who may surface every 10–20 minutes). There is frequent touching between mother and calf.

Nursing

Calves have to eat in Hawaii, even though adults do not. Fortunately, their food supply is big, mobile, and always at their side. Humpback calves nurse (that is, they rely entirely on mother's milk) throughout their first winter, and through much of their first year of life. The process of weaning is believed to begin between six and ten months of age on the summer grounds, where more solid food is taken, and ends with separation from the mother after the first feeding season.

Nursing behavior has been observed in Hawaii, with the calf poking its mouth up towards the mother's mammary glands on each side of the genital area on her belly. At times puffs of escaped milk can be seen quickly dissipating into the sea. This activity can occur while the pair are stationary or traveling — clearly a skill that saves on the migration time. However, beyond a handful of underwater encounters with nursing whales, we have no insight into the schedule, duration of bouts, or overall amount of time a mother must spend nursing her calf.

Vulnerability to Boat Collisions

The common humpback mother-and-newborn behavior pattern — of the adult lying stationary beneath the surface for long periods while the calf surfaces alone — makes calves the most likely victims of boat-whale collisions.

With its small profile and almost invisible blows, a calf can be very difficult to spot (even when looking) and especially in any kind of rough sea conditions. Such collisions, causing serious injury to the whale and damage to the boat, occur each year (*see Chapter 7*).

Play

Baby humpbacks play. Mimicry of the mother, or the male escort, is common newborn behavior in Hawaii. Calf surface behaviors, including flippering, spyhops, rolling, tail slaps, tail lashes, tail throws, head lunges, full breaches, and belly flops, are all activities seen in adults *(see Actions and Postures)*.

The calves also play with objects in their environment, such as sticks in a tide-line, boats, or a diver. However, they do not play with each other. The mothers seem to forbid this or, at least, do not allow the circumstances for calves to interact. Whether this has more to do with the mother's reproductive strategy or the calf's survival is not known.

Calves imitated their mothers by repeating the behavior immediately after the mother performed it, including breaching, tail throwing, tail slapping and flippering. They also imitated the escort whale, performing head lunging, throat expansion, chin slapping and bubblestreaming.

**Glockner-Ferrari and Ferrari
1985**

Calves copy much of the adult behavior around them.

Mothers and calves are relatively quiet (compared to males), but grunt-like sounds have been recorded from calves.

Mother/Calf Communication

When listening (with a hydrophone) near a mother with calf, the over-riding impression is that they are both very quiet! Over the years, single, grunt-like vocalizations from the calf (and in one case loud continuous sounds made by calf, mother or both) have been reported, but these were generally considered exceptional.

A recent study in Hawaii, however, suggests that calf vocalizations may be more common than previously thought. In this project, grunt-like sounds were regularly recorded in both mother/calf and mother/calf/escort groups, and from both male and female calves. The function of the sounds is not known, but suggestions include calling the mother, an alarm call, or a response to something new. There is currently no evidence that the exchange is two-way (that is, returned by the mother).

In contrast to the brash loudness of singers or males in competitive groups, mothers and calves seem to be at the other end of the audio scale. This topic joins the many others awaiting researchers' attention and raises at least three good questions:

- Are mothers and calves indeed relatively quiet, or are we missing something?

- Is quietness a behavior to remain undetected by passing males?

- As the calf is virtually always in physical and/or visual contact with the mother, are calls necessary?

Non-song vocalizations (attributed to the calf) were recorded in 65% of calf pods. These vocalizations were most common in lone mother/calf pairs.

Zoidis et al.
2008

Physical contact is very important between a mother and her newborn. Here a young calf lies on its immobile mother resting at the surface.

JIM DARLING

The Calf And The Escort(s)

In Hawaiian waters, humpback mothers are usually accompanied by a male escort. (The escort role is not that of a father spending time with his offspring.) The specific male in this escort role often changes, either voluntarily as it just ups and departs, through competition for the position (with other males), or when ditched by the female. At times, the escort sings while accompanying the mother and calf. At other times he may pursue the mother. How does the calf relate to all this?

For the most part, it appears the calf is not harmed by all the adult activity. This tentative conclusion comes solely from the observation that such adult action around newborns is very common and there are lots of young calves. So, if a mother finds herself mixed up in a group of males, at least it does not spell sure disaster for the calf. There have been several reports of a calf seemingly ignored when the adults (mother and escort) were otherwise engaged, and others where the calf surfaced alongside the escort rather than its mother — but these are rare, with no indication of the loss or death of the calves or of other negative effects. (However, it should be clear by now that researchers do not see everything that occurs on the breeding grounds.)

The fact is that we have little scientific insight into how the calf is affected by the surrounding social melee. This activity may use up critical energy reserves and even cause injury or, on the other hand, it may play a significant role in calf development and learning. It could be both, with the behavior of the mother around males changing with the age of the calf.

Escorts: Are They Hired Guns?

When a humpback whale mother and calf are alone, they expend a certain amount of energy, when escorted by a single male they expend more energy (as indicated by behavioral changes), and when surrounded by multiple males substantially more energy again. Yet, considering that energy may be the female's most precious asset, the most common social arrangement is the middle option above — the mother, calf, and escort group. Why?

One explanation proposed is that the mother may associate with a single escort as a trade-off — the single escort raises her energy expenditure

Newborn calves spend a lot of their time racing alongside mother just ahead of one or many males. Some speculate that mothers accept a single male escort as he serves to protect her and her newborn from further harassment.

to some degree; however, multiple escorts have the potential for a far greater negative impact. By associating with a single escort, the mother may minimize harassment by other males and the even greater energy expenditure that would entail. This behavior pattern has been described in other mammals with similar female/male associations, and these escort males have been called 'hired guns' or 'bodyguards.'

Is this what is happening in Hawaiian waters? If so, what does the male get out of the arrangement? Does mere presence lead to preference when the female comes into estrus? One twist in the idea is that, as single males also escort a female without a calf, this 'hired gun' behavior (if that is what it is) may be a general female strategy, not just something mothers do.

As escorts join the mother/calf pair, the energy demands increase, especially in the case of multiple escorts versus single escorts.

Cartwright
1999

Juveniles

One segment of the social mix of humpbacks in Hawaiian waters is the juveniles, also referred to as sub-adults. This category includes recently weaned yearlings and whales several years old, before they reach sexual maturity.

There have been no studies focusing on this juvenile 'subculture' of the Hawaiian population. At least some yearlings make their first winter migration to Hawaii with their mothers, and then separate during the breeding assembly. They have little choice but to begin their independent lives in the Islands. Slightly older juvenile whales are also present — presumably having followed the adults during the migration. At the same time, there is evidence that not all juvenile humpbacks make the entire migration.

What insight researchers have on the young animals comes almost entirely from opportunistic observations during studies of mothers and calves or of mature whales involved in mating behavior. The juveniles (usually identified by being bigger than a calf, independent, yet smaller

The juveniles are a little-known segment of the Hawaiian humpback population. Here, a yearling eyes photographer Flip Nicklin.

than an adult) are often found on the periphery of other social groups — following the action but not intimately involved. These smaller whales have specifically been reported:

- Following competitive or surface active groups
- With adult males
- Near adult male/female pairs
- With mother and newborn
- Accompanying each other (in pairs)
- Alone (in one observation, a lone sub-adult was identified as female)

Hints of one behavior pattern of juvenile humpback whales are just beginning to emerge — their interaction with adult males. One study noted two occasions where yearling-sized whales were with an adult male and engaged in apparent sexual activity; at one point the penis of

155

> *They (juvenile male
> and adult male) were
> rubbing against each other,
> twirling and swimming upside
> down and rolling together,
> 'caressing' each other
> with their flippers.*
>
> Glockner-Ferrari and Ferrari
> 1985

the sub-adult was extended and rubbed against the genital slit of the adult. There is also an observation where a sub-adult was the apparent object of a fight between adult males. Another study noted a much smaller animal, presumed to be a yearling or a juvenile, with an adult singer.

Other, somewhat incongruous, whale behavior seen in Hawaii is attributed to juveniles. In one case, a juvenile was observed making feeding lunges through a school of mackerel. Also, many of the whales that approach and focus on boats and divers, at times swimming around them for hours, are young animals — likely either intrigued or bored — left out of the more serious activities in the region. All in all, however, the juvenile years (between leaving their mother and becoming sexually mature) are near blank pages in our story of humpback whale society.

Our understanding of young humpback whales is just beginning. Remarkably abundant in some areas during peak season — one comes across mothers and new calves literally every few minutes when boating — their behavior reflects both the necessities of first-year survival as governed by the mother, and the natural play and curiosity of any young mammal. Great questions remain: Where and when are they born? How do they communicate? Why don't they associate with other mothers and new-borns? Are rowdy males a threat to their survival? When weaned, how do they learn to be an adult?

Abundant, healthy humpback whale calves like those we see in Hawaii bode well for the future of this population.

Newborns and Juveniles

Quick Info

*When and where do humpback whale
births occur?*

A humpback whale birth has not been observed.
However, there is much circumstantial evidence,
including observation of tiny creased calves and
placental material, to indicate births occur during the
migration and in the winter assembly in Hawaii.

What are the priorities of mother and newborn?

Mothers need to maintain circumstances that are
optimal for rest, nursing, and protection of the young,
including (at least sometimes) avoidance of sexually
active males. Mothers with a newborn maintain
separation from breeding activity by staying in shallow
waters, just outside reefs.

Why shallow waters?

It is speculated that mothers with young calves stay in shallow waters to avoid sexually active males, rough offshore sea conditions, and/or predators.

Are predators an issue for new mothers?

Killer whales, likely the most formidable predator of humpback whales and common in summer grounds, are rarely seen in Hawaii. However, there are occasional observations of false killer whales (15-ft dolphins) harassing and attacking humpback mothers with a calf. Sharks follow and eat sick or dead whales, but there is no indication they attack healthy animals.

What do newborn humpbacks do?

Newborn humpback whales spend a great deal of time traveling with the mother. They also rest, play, nurse, explore objects in their environment, and stay out of the way when adult males join their mother. Play includes mimicking many of the actions of mother and escort males.

How do the juveniles, who have left mom but are not yet sexually mature, behave?

Knowledge of the behavior of juvenile or sub-adult whales is limited. They are certainly present and often found on the periphery of competitive or other adult groups, or in the company of adult males, including singers. Apparent sexual activity has been observed in these adult male/juvenile groups.

Chapter 7

Whales and Us

The relationship of our modern society with humpback whales has been short but dramatic. After thousands of years of coexistence, we developed the technology that would allow us to catch and kill them en masse. Then, it took us less than a single human lifetime to nearly wipe them from the face of the planet. When whalers could not find any more, they moved on to other, more plentiful, species, and humpback whales were only then protected (in 1966).

Since then, our relationship with whales has swung decidedly in the opposite direction, towards a time of unprecedented interest in the living animal — interest in conservation, research, education, and whale watching. The more we have come to know the whales, the more fascinating they have become, with whales now part of that select group of animals that hold exceptional interest and inspiration for humans.

So what does the future hold? Will the pendulum swing again, as the numbers of humpback whales and their conflicts with human endeavors increase? Have the animals gained a permanent level of respect? Or, regardless of our respect, will depletion of ocean life and marine pollution and traffic have the same impact as whaling? This chapter looks at our relationships with humpback whales — past and present.

How Are Whales Doing?

Arguably, the most common question asked about whales has to do with
their status. There is a broad awareness that whales were hunted to near
extinction and many are on endangered species lists *(see Appendix)*. There
have been decades of high-publicity campaigns to save the whales from
the threats of whaling, capture, loss of habitat or prey, collisions, and
harassment. However, it is not always clear if these campaigns have been
successful, if progress has been made, if the whales are indeed being saved.

For humpbacks, the pendulum has swung from whaling times, when they were seen only as a commodity, to a time of enormous interest in the living animal.

There is no single or simple answer to this question, and certainly not one that applies to the more than 80 species of whales and dolphins. The answer may even be different for populations of the same species living in different parts of the world. Some whales are abundant, some were at endangered levels but with protection numbers are increasing, some are at endangered levels and seem stuck there, and one species has probably become extinct in the last few years. The category a particular population of whales falls into generally depends on the interplay of three things:

- Its recent relationship with humans (if the object of whaling, how many survived).

- Its reproductive potential — how fast they can reproduce.

- The health of its current environment, especially food quality and availability, and the level of pollution.

How Are the 'Hawaiian' Humpback Whales Doing?

The humpback whales off Hawaiian shores currently remain on endangered species lists; however, they have turned the corner in their recovery. All indications are that the numbers in Hawaii, and generally worldwide, have increased steadily since whaling stopped. So, the whales seen in Hawaii are doing well — especially when compared to some other species and populations worldwide. However, to place this statement in context, we need to look at the past, the present, and think about the future of these animals.

Hawaii's humpbacks have recovered well with protection from whaling. This recovery is mirrored in most other humpback whale populations around the world.

GORDON PIKE, DFO Canada

Whaling of humpback whales legally ended in 1966, although illegal Soviet whaling continued into the next decade.

The 1900s

Whaling

Through the first sixty or so years of the twentieth century, humpback whale populations were decimated worldwide in one of the greatest massacres of mammals in human history. The North Pacific, and whales we now know as 'Hawaiian' humpbacks, were no exception. The best indication of the efficiency of this hunt was that most whaling operations were abandoned, moved, or switched to other species even before humpback whales were protected internationally in 1966. That is, the most experienced and motivated whale finders in the world — the whalers — could not find any more to hunt.

It is not known how many humpbacks the whalers left in the North Pacific or, for that matter, how many lived in this ocean prior to the onset of whaling. One rough estimate often used is that there were about 15,000 humpback whales in the North Pacific before commercial whaling. Equally rough estimates suggest that 1,200 to 1,400 humpbacks may have survived the whaling operations, or about 10 percent of the pre-whaling numbers. It is important to emphasize the back-of-the-envelope nature of these estimates, and few researchers would be surprised if the actual numbers were double these in both cases. But also, few would argue that the North Pacific humpback whale population was reduced to a small remnant of pre-whaling levels.

Additional humpback whales were still being killed (by the Soviet fleet) in the North Pacific years after international protection in 1966.

Doroshenko
2000

Recovery

Since commercial whaling ended and the species was protected, humpback whales appear to have made a steady comeback in most of their traditional

Evidence of failed harpoon shots are still seen on humpbacks in Hawaiian waters.

JIM DARLING

North Pacific ranges. It is apparent, in the case of North Pacific humpback whales, that a viable population survived the whaling and that their food supply has been adequate over the last few decades. Moreover, as we learned in an earlier chapter, this species has a high reproductive potential — with up to a calf per year for some females. This pattern appears to hold true for many humpback whale populations around the world. We have two concrete signs of this recovery in the North Pacific. (1) Estimates of population size have increased steadily since counts began. And (2) in the last decade or so, humpback whales have re-inhabited traditional ranges around the Pacific Rim empty of the species since whaling times.

The Numbers

- **1970s.** The first estimates of humpback whales in Hawaiian waters suggested a population in the low to mid hundreds. (However, these estimates were based on brief aerial and vessel surveys and could have easily underestimated the population size.)

- **Late 1970s/early 1980s.** The first calculations based on photo-identification of individual whales off Maui produced estimates ranging around 1,000 to 2,000 whales visiting Hawaii over a winter.

- **Early 1990s.** Photo-identification techniques estimated the Hawaiian population at 3,000 to 5,000. A second study (about the same time) estimated 6,000 to 8,000 humpbacks in the entire North Pacific, with 4,000 of those visiting Hawaii.

- **Mid 2000s.** The most recent estimate (developed from an ocean-wide survey known as SPLASH conducted from 2004 to 2006) indicates that approximately 20,000 humpbacks now populate the North Pacific, with half of those visiting Hawaii.

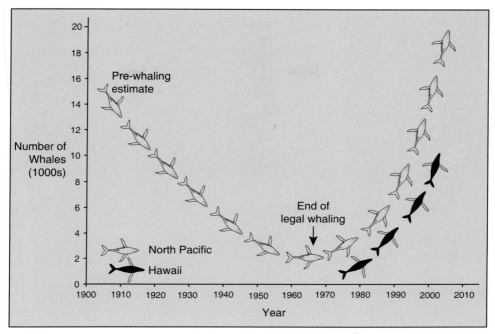

The numbers of humpbacks in Hawaii have increased steadily since whaling stopped. Abundance estimates have gone from a low of 1,000 to 2,000 in the mid-1970s (and first surveys) to 10,000 today. The most recent estimate for the entire North Pacific humpback population is about 20,000 animals. Interpretation of the status of the population (although obviously increasing) is problematic in that the starting-point (or pre-whaling) number of 15,000 shown here was no more than an educated guess.

That is, the numbers of humpback whales in Hawaii have increased steadily from the late 1970s through the 1990s, and into the mid 2000s. In that time, the numbers of humpback whales visiting Hawaii apparently increased at least five-fold. In the last fifteen years alone, the humpback population in Hawaii has doubled.

18,302 represented the best estimate of overall abundance of humpback whales in the North Pacific, excluding calves. Over 50% of this population was estimated to winter in Hawaiian waters.

Calambokidis et al.
2008

Not All Whale Populations Are Recovering

North Pacific right whale — Hawaii, 1979

The positive outlook for humpback whales arising from increasing numbers and return to traditional ranges does not, unfortunately, apply to all whales. Certain populations and species remain on the critical list, their future uncertain. Extinction is a real possibility for some. A few examples follow.

- The Yangtze River dolphin, a species that lives only in one river in China, was on a downhill slide for decades due to habitat destruction. Despite conservation efforts, it was declared extinct in 2007.

- The North Pacific right whale (officially protected in 1937) is so rare that a single sighting warrants a scientific publication — it probably numbers only several hundreds. Two sightings of lone right whales have been made in Hawaii in the last thirty years, mixing with humpback whales.

- The North Atlantic right whales (officially protected in 1937), numbering some 300 animals, are living in the midst of major

Western gray whale — Japan, 1993

shipping lanes and fisheries activity, where vessel strikes and entanglements take a critical toll each year.

- The western North Pacific (Asian) gray whales (protected from commercial whaling in 1948) are now represented by a tiny remnant population of about 100 animals with primary feeding grounds overlapping the largest oil and gas development in eastern Asia.

- Other populations of whales at risk, not generally subject to intensive whaling, include killer whales in Washington State and British Columbia and beluga whales in the Gulf of St. Lawrence. These whales are higher on the food chain than the baleen whales and, among other things, are facing increasing health problems from toxins transferred from their industrialized environment.

The simple survival, much less recovery, of these and other whale populations will be an uphill battle.

Hawaiian Humpbacks Today

With a turbulent past behind them, humpback whales in Hawaii are now protected, watched, filmed, studied, and celebrated. They are a topic of school curricula, their songs are broadcast live globally on websites and they are the basis of profitable businesses. They have marine sanctuaries named after them, and are the official state marine mammal of Hawaii. They have both US Federal and Hawaii State government representatives at most whale meetings concerning their protection.

Today, humpback whales in Hawaii (and everywhere else) are an enormous attraction for both the general public and scientists. They are protected, studied, and celebrated.

At the same time, even with all this attention and good will, humpback whales die each year from being entangled in fishing gear and hit by vessels. And these, to be frank, are minor problems when compared to looming threats of renewal of whaling, conflicts over food supply and habitat, or global climate change. The world of humpback whales is anything but secure. For the remainder of this chapter we will look at both the promise and the threats facing humpback whales in the first decades of the twenty-first century.

The Promise — Science And Education

Protection

Humpback whales continue to be protected from whaling by the International Whaling Commission (IWC) and indirectly through a ban on trade of (whaling) products through the Convention on International Trade in Endangered Species of Wild Fauna and Flora (CITES) *(see Appendix)*. (Currently both agreements are being tested by whaling countries.)

Humpback whales are also protected, to varying degrees, by acts or laws of the countries whose boundary waters they visit. The strongest protection is in United States waters with the US Marine Mammal Protection and Endangered Species Acts *(see Appendix)*. Therefore, humpback whales with breeding grounds in Hawaii and feeding grounds in Alaska currently have some of the highest protection of any whales (for that matter of any wildlife) in the world.

There are, however, two caveats regarding present Hawaiian humpback protection. (1) It is not permanent and the whales can be "down-listed" at any time — that is, given reduced protection or taken off protected species lists (this discussion has already begun due to the increase in numbers). (2) When the whales we see in Hawaii travel elsewhere in the Pacific, such as along the Asian coast, the level of protection decreases to, at most, the voluntary IWC agreement not to hunt them (currently indications are this is generally upheld).

Science

As this book testifies, the progress in our scientific understanding of living whales over the last thirty or so years is extraordinary and continuing enthusiastically. The lives and world of these animals are being gradually revealed, as we are literally learning more every day.

There is a steady stream of scientific papers on humpback whales from locations such as Hawaii, Australia, Alaska, the US Eastern Seaboard, the West Indies, Central Africa, Madagascar, Brazil, Ecuador, and others, investigating the whole range of behavioral subjects in this book (as well as other aspects of their biology). Indeed, it is challenging to keep up with the worldwide progress.

The Hawaiian Islands Humpback Whale National Marine Sanctuary

MEAGAN JONES

In 1997, the US and Hawaii governments designated the Hawaiian Islands Humpback Whale National Marine Sanctuary — the nation's twelfth marine sanctuary.

Its purposes are to protect humpback whales and their habitat within the sanctuary; to educate and interpret for the public the relationship of humpback whales and the Hawaiian Islands marine environment; to manage human uses of the sanctuary consistent with the Hawaiian Islands National Marine Sanctuary Act and the National Marine Sanctuary Act; and to identify marine resources and ecosystems of national significance for possible inclusion in the sanctuary.

In fact, humpback whales are currently protected equally inside and outside of the sanctuary boundaries. However, the designation is important symbolically, reflecting the importance of these animals in local and national views.

Research programs worldwide are describing the lives of humpback whales. A student from Italy, in Hawaii for the whale season, ponders spectrographs of song composition.

A search of biological abstracts conducted just before this book went to press listed over 200 papers that include new information on humpback whales published since the year 2000.

Not only is there a growing number of researchers, in more locations, but new technologies are opening doors never dreamed possible a few years ago. It was advances in technology (now seemingly ancient) such as the development of the 35 mm SLR camera and of the hydrophone, in the 1950s and 60s, that led to the first steps in the study of living whales. Now, with sophisticated genetic techniques, satellite tracking, and other 'smart' tags (including placing a camera on the whales themselves), it's clear we have barely begun to achieve what is possible in terms of exploring and understanding the lives of these animals. There is lots of work to do — the field is wide open.

The singer and
his song have
intrigued scientists
(and the public) for
decades.

Education

Whales fascinate us. They capture our imaginations, kids and adults alike, all over the world. The reason is not entirely clear—perhaps it is the combination of the mystery of the unknown oceans, and the unimaginable scale and exceptional grace of the animals. Perhaps it is a result of Jules Verne's *20,000 Leagues Under the Sea* and Herman Melville's *Moby Dick*, or Jacques Cousteau and the *National Geographic* photographs and films of wild whales, where reality has indeed proven more incredible than the fantasy of the early works. Whatever the reasons, they have been compelling to our species.

There is an insatiable desire worldwide for popular and educational materials featuring whales: articles and books, radio and TV shows, school curricula, and community whale festivals. Humpback whales, due to their regular appearance in nearshore locales such as Hawaii combined with their propensity for surface behavior and acrobatics that attract our attention, are one of the best-known whales and the subject of much global media attention.

Most importantly, and as any educator will attest, this interest in whales is often the key to the introduction to other marine life and environmental issues. And it even leads a few to careers in marine research and conservation.

Whales are the perfect catalyst for marine-education programs. Kids from Maui schools enthusiastically recreate a humpback's tail markings (used for individual photo-identification) on life-sized tails (measured during a research program). This took place at Whale Quest Kapalua, a public event on Maui.

JASON A. MOORE

Whale watching is a hugely successful industry and a powerful economic argument against whaling. It also provides an opportunity for increasing public awareness of our oceans and the issues and challenges ahead.

Whale Watching

Whale watching, now huge, began modestly in the 1950s in California when a few boats went to watch gray whales migrate along the coast. It has since grown into a worldwide industry, existing in virtually every country with a coastline.

The latest statistics on whale watching are now about ten years old. At the end of the 1990s, whale watching was responsible for a global income estimated at over one billion dollars annually, with nine million clients in eighty-seven countries and territories, in 492 communities. In Hawaii during the 1998–99 season, for instance, fifty-two boats took out 370,000 passengers, with $11.2 million in ticket sales alone; with peripheral sales, income was an estimated $20 million.

Whale watching is not only popular and profitable. It also provides a powerful economic argument for the sustainable use of living whales versus killed whales (and their one-time use as meat and fertilizer). Whale watching has become a significant factor in the economic survival and growth of small coastal communities around the world.

Whale watching also has enormous unquantifiable benefits as a medium of awareness, education, and experience. Perhaps the most significant contribution in the long run is that it draws millions of people to the ocean and introduces them to two-thirds of our planet — something that would otherwise be an unlikely occurrence for many. A close encounter with a wild whale is enthralling, inspiring, and rather than satiating, often leads to more trips, more locations, a desire to see different species and behavior, and to learn more about our oceans.

Approaching Whales in Hawaii

Federal and State regulations prohibit any unauthorized approach to humpback whales in the Hawaiian Islands within 100 yards (90 m) on the water and below 1,000 feet (305 m) in the air.

Researchers that make closer approaches as part of their studies require both Federal (National Marine Fisheries Service) and Hawaii State (Department of Land and Natural Resources) permits.

Researchers must fly yellow flags with permit numbers from their boats, or if working from aircraft, must have contacted enforcement personnel prior to the activity.

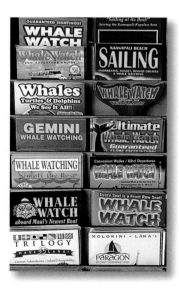

JIM DARLING

INSERT: ED LYMAN, HIHWNMS/NOAA FISHERIES MMHSRP

Humpbacks die each year entangled in fishing and mooring gear. In Hawaii, some of those entangled are freed, but not all can be reached or saved.

The Threats

Even with humpbacks making a healthy recovery, there are enormous challenges ahead in the conservation and management of this (and all wild) species. All have to do with the consequences of human development and/or commerce — that is, conflicts, directly or indirectly, with human activities. Following are a few issues discussed daily in whale research and conservation circles, divided into threats to individuals and threats to populations overall.

Threats to Individuals: Entanglements and Collisions

Today, the mostly likely threats to an otherwise healthy humpback whale involve entanglements with fishing gear and collisions with vessels — both on the rise as whale populations recover.

These entanglement and/or collision threats generally affect individuals more than the population overall. This is not meant to downplay the issue in any way, as they are clearly traumatic, painful, and/or deadly to that animal. However, these are threats that affect one individual at a time versus those that can affect the viability of a population in general, as discussed below.

It is worth noting that, in highly endangered whale populations, the death of just one individual — particularly a mature female — can have a significant impact on the health of the entire population, so these threats should not be taken lightly.

Entanglements

It is not known how many humpback whales are lost to entanglements with fishing and mooring gear each year. Certainly, every season, entangled whales are found in Hawaii. As this location is the furthest from the greatest overlap between whales and intensive fishing activity (in their summer grounds), it's likely these are a small segment of those afflicted.

At times, the entangled whales are located and cut free, a service currently conducted by the Hawaiian Islands Humpback Whale National Marine Sanctuary personnel. At other times, the whales move out of range and/or the damage is so severe they will not recover. Most of the entanglements are net or line wrapped around the flukes, flippers, or head; on occasion, the whales are actually towing mooring buoys. The sources of the problem are active fishing operations, as well as the tons of discarded and lost gear and garbage floating at sea.

From 2002 to 2008, as many as 35 different humpback whales were found entangled (in fishing gear, marine debris, mooring systems) in Hawaii.

Lyman and Mattila
2008

Two sets of the fishing gear removed from whales in Hawaii were traced back to crab/cod pot gear used in the Aleutian Islands.

Lyman and Mattila
2007

MARK FERRARI, CENTER FOR WHALE STUDIES

Vessel–Whale Collisions

Each year collisions between vessels and humpback whales occur throughout their range. These often result in the injury or death of the whale, and significant damage to the vessel.

The number of collisions reported in Hawaii in winter is increasing, and it is likely these are only a portion of those that actually occur. (The increase in reports may be partially due to improved record keeping in recent years.) The density of the whales in peak season can be so great that it is amazing collisions are not more frequent. In most cases, the whale is not seen again, so the extent of its injuries is not known. In other cases, it is clear the whale is bleeding and in serious trouble.

The most likely whale victims in Hawaii are the newborn calves, which must surface several times to mother's once. These small calves are easy to miss, even when watching for them, if moving at typical

Newborn humpbacks are especially vulnerable to collisions with vessels, as is illustrated by this calf sliced by a boat propeller. Such collisions are on the increase.

vessel speeds of 20 knots or more. Other whale victims are those sleeping motionless on or just under the surface, apparently only semi-conscious.

The solution is low tech — lower speed in the areas of high whale density. This would solve much of the problem, but is not currently regulated; indeed, in Hawaii just the opposite is happening with the introduction of high-speed super ferries between the main islands.

During the 2006–07 winter season, there were at least six confirmed collisions between boats and whales in Hawaii; in the 2007–08 season there were 12 reported ship-strikes.

Schofield
2007, 2008

185

With numbers of humpback whales increasing, they have the full attention of whaling interests. More whales will also inevitably result in more conflicts with human activity.

Threats to Populations: Hunting, Food, and Habitat

Population-scale threats tend to affect more than one whale at a time, and may weaken or destroy an entire population or even species. Humpback whales have in their favor the strengths of being a global species, being flexible about food type, and having a high reproductive rate. With these assets, humpbacks may be able to biologically dodge and weave their way through some of these threats for a time, but without human intervention on their behalf, eventually the viability of populations will be compromised.

Commercial Whaling

Currently, there is no legal whaling of humpback whales in the North Pacific. However, this is a temporary state, with no guarantee that whaling will not occur in the future. The whaling interests are alive and well and waiting, taking every opportunity to re-establish the industry in locations and with species not considered as endangered as humpback whales — and humpback whales are on the verge of losing their endangered status. With growing human populations, and the collapse of traditional fisheries around the world, it would be naïve to think these animals will not again be targeted.

A count of endangered humpback whales is revealing a comeback so convincing that marine scientists are pondering the controversial question: Is it time for the whales, hunted to near-extinction in the 20th century, to have less protection . . .

San Jose Mercury News
June 8, 2007

The Down-Listing and Whaling Debate

Due to the increase in numbers of humpback whales in the North Pacific, the debate has begun as to whether or not they should be taken off endangered species lists — that is, down-listed to a lesser level of protection. Among other things, this decision to down-list would make a renewal of whaling much easier.

Most researchers view this situation with mixed emotions. Endangered species acts and laws are based only on numbers (not on how much we know about the animals and their biological requirements). On one hand, it's very positive that the numbers of humpback whales have increased, and few would argue that the endangered designation should be for truly endangered species. On the other hand, should this rise in numbers mean that humpbacks are all of a sudden fair game?

JIM DARLING

Humpback whales engulf masses of small fish with great efficiency (by expanding throat pleats to create a huge maw, as shown above). Conflicts with human fisheries may be unavoidable in the future.

Competition with Human Fisheries

Humans and humpback whales share some of the same prey, including such species as herring and sardines (pilchards). Currently, in the case of North Pacific humpback whales and fishermen, there is apparently enough to go around, but will this overlap be a factor in the future of the whales? Odds are the answer is yes, in one or more of the following ways:

- With increasing numbers of whales and reduced fish stocks, the whales and fishermen compete in the same areas, with entanglement in gear an issue.

- The over-fishing and disappearance of fish stocks, of which there are many examples, force the whales to move to other regions or species that may be less than optimal.

- Whales are blamed for the reduction in fish stocks as a justification to renew whaling.

All three of these scenarios are occurring today to some extent. The last of these is an ongoing debate at the IWC, with the whaling factions arguing relentlessly that the whales are eating all "our" fish — so we need to hunt them. There is no scientific basis for this claim, but it is not unusual for us to blame other species for fishery troubles — particularly a species that is perceived as having more commercial value dead than alive.

Humpback whales range over such large (and often remote) areas that it is nearly impossible to document potential problems, much less monitor them. Below, humpbacks feed amongst thousands of seabirds in the Bering Sea.

Human activities and pollution are altering the environment of whales. These range from overt acts such as harmful military sonar, to a myriad of more subtle and long- term actions that may affect habitat and food supply.

Changing Natural Habitats: Pollution to Climate Change

Human activities are changing the habitats of whales in myriad ways, ranging from increasing marine traffic, to industrial development, to chemical and noise pollution, to climate change. These will have an impact on whales either directly through destruction of habitat or indirectly through influences on their prey.

In a few cases, the causes of lethal impacts are blatantly obvious — such as the loss of the Yangtze River dolphin to river industry (one observer likened it to dolphins trying to live on the median of a free-way), belugas in the Gulf of St. Lawrence dying of diseases directly linked to pollutant chemicals, or naval sonar activities leading to whale strandings.

In most cases, though, it can be extremely difficult to recognize and measure the non-lethal impacts of habitat pollution and change. Our limited knowledge of natural behavior patterns makes it hard to identify critical changes, and the huge, multinational ranges many whales travel over make it impossible to be aware of all the circumstances they encounter. So, by the time a whale strands (or dies), it is often too late to do much about it as the causes may be too far away in time and/or location.

In Hawaii, a few examples of habitat change are increasing vessel traffic (including fast ferries that speed through breeding grounds), run-off from agricultural lands clouding near-shore waters, harbor construction, and naval exercises that include use of strikingly loud sonar sounds. Remember, however, that most individual whales are only present in Hawaii for several weeks before returning to feeding grounds where other habitat issues dog both them and their prey.

Cumulative Impacts — Adding Them All Together

Many small changes to whale behavior, themselves insignificant, may accumulate and develop into a significant threat. Seemingly minor impacts may include a whale researcher disturbing a whale for a few minutes, then a whale-watch boat, then the noise of a passing tugboat and barge, a near miss of a ferry, slightly less food due to a fishing operation, having to swim around (or get entangled in) a discarded fishing net, then moving away from an area due to tolerable but bothersome noise levels. The concern is that these cumulative impacts may affect the health of the individual over time through stress-related disease and/or more energy expenditure and less energy input than is optimal.

Extreme Noise Pollution: Naval Active Sonar Systems

Military active sonar emits intense sound waves that travel through tens to hundreds of miles of ocean to locate enemy submarines. Such capability requires an extremely loud sound source — so loud that it changes the behavior of whales, and can even result in their injury and death.

Some toothed whales appear to be especially sensitive to these sound levels, with multiple examples of strandings, bleeding from brain and ears, and death documented worldwide.

The impact of these sounds on baleen whales, including humpback whales, is less clear. One study was conducted in Hawaii to determine the impact of naval sonar (at less than full strength) on humpback whales. Whereas no immediate stranding or deaths occurred, the sounds did change behavior, causing some whales to stop singing and other whales to lengthen their song during sonar playback.

Climate Change

JIM DARLING

There is now no doubt that pollution from human technology is changing ecological systems worldwide. The ultimate impacts that global warming will have on specific species like humpback whales are near impossible to predict due to the complexity of ocean systems. However, a rise of only a few degrees in ocean temperature could affect humpback whales by causing, for example:

- Changes in ocean circulation and thus plankton and the overall food web. Humpback whales are doing well with the status quo, so any change will undoubtedly impact them in some way.

- Movement of the whales away from the Hawaiian Islands so as to stay within the apparent optimal range of water temperature they seek during winter.

- Disruption of the primary food of potential predators like the killer whale or false killer whale, thereby forcing them to target humpback whales more than occurs today.

One of the reasons biologists are so concerned about this problem is that we have no idea of the outcome. It is a cliché now, but this is truly a global experiment with all species the subjects. Change is the only sure result, with the final stable state anyone's guess.

So, Why Don't We Just Protect Whales?

There are three substantial human forces defining, or trying to define, our relationship with whales today.

There are the whaling interests, which view whales as a commodity. These include factions in countries such as Japan and Norway, with abstinence-type assistance — that is, no objection — from other countries. These factions are well-funded, sophisticated, and determined to resume whaling operations.

Second are the ocean-based industries and activities, including fisheries, oil exploitation, and military, that increasingly find themselves in conflict over space and resources used by whales. These industries rarely (if ever) want to harm the whales, but the animals are in the way of activity deemed more important. Pollution, habitat loss, noise, entanglements, and cumulative effects are all issues.

A third, and potentially very powerful, positive force is the collective voice of people who recognize the value of protecting whales and their habitat — whether it be for maintaining a culture, making a living, teaching our kids, or better understanding our planet. This force is rooted in people who have come to realize that healthy whale populations, while desirable in and of themselves, also reflect a healthy world.

These forces meet on a regular basis. The whales, and critical ocean habitat, don't always win. Perhaps the greatest threat to humpback whales (and true for all wildlife) is our lack of understanding of their ecological and social requirements — what these animals really need to stay alive and healthy. Without this knowledge, the best intentions are unlikely to solve the conflicts that are inevitable. This is the challenge for researchers and educators.

What's Next For Humpbacks?

Few experienced biologists would dare predict the future of complex natural systems and the species they support. We have learned on one hand of their fragility and, on the other, of their flexibility, adaptability, and resilience. However, one would be hard pressed to find examples of any large wild animal found to be in conflict with human endeavor, or seen as a commercial commodity, that is far from jeopardy. This makes the future of humpback whales particularly tenuous.

We are in the midst of an era when humpback whales have received the best of human attention. They are recovering globally and, unlike some other whale species, the potential for healthy wild populations may still exist. Humpback whales, in regions like Hawaii, have returned our favor in spades. They have helped bring conservation issues home to us. They have supported our livelihoods, inspired our science, art, music, and literature. They have charged the imaginations of our kids. They have made us want to know more about the world we live in — from diatom to copepod, to sardine, to whale.

The decision to stop whaling allowed the recovery of humpback whales, and many populations are thriving, but this relatively peaceful time is likely not permanent.

However, the jury (that is, us) that will determine their future is still out. On one hand, there has never been more human energy directed towards research, public awareness, and conservation. On the other, the fundamental problems whales face — pollution and habitat loss and whaling due to growth of human populations, industry, and markets — have not gone away, are not being resolved, and indeed are growing. The conservation of humpback whales, as with other wild species, will depend entirely on: (1) the will to act; and (2) acquiring the knowledge to act wisely. Neither, alone, will protect the whales.

Today, humpback whales are in a relative calm — between commercial whaling, and the potential destruction of the natural systems that support them (along with probably more whaling). During this period there is the urgency to learn as much as we can about whales — to actually understand their environmental and social requirements, to recognize their value as living animals, and to work to protect them.

195

We are literally dipping our toes into the world of humpback whales, with the promise of many more insights and discoveries awaiting us.

Whales and Us

Quick Info

Are humpback whales in Hawaii recovering?

Humpback whales in Hawaii, and in many regions worldwide, are recovering relatively well (compared to some other whale species), with numbers increasing steadily since whaling ended.

What laws protect them?

Humpback whales are protected from whaling internationally through the IWC (International Whaling Commission) and from illegal trade by CITES (Convention on International Trade in Endangered Species of Wild Fauna and Flora). In addition, the United States has strong laws — the Marine Mammal Protection Act and the Endangered Species Act — that protect these animals in US waters.

What are the greatest current threats to the humpback whales seen in Hawaii?

The greatest current, day-to-day threats to these whales are entanglements with fishing gear or marine garbage and collisions with vessels.

Do we know enough about humpback whales to provide meaningful management in conflicts with industry or renewed whaling?

Unfortunately, no. While our knowledge of humpback whales is greater than for many other whale species, our understanding of their habitat, food, social, and behavioral requirements is not yet adequate to manage major conflicts with humans.

What does the future look like for humpback whales?

As human population and industry expand, it is very likely conflicts with whales (and with all wildlife) will increase. The whalers are standing by. One safe prediction is that the goal of conserving healthy populations of whales will become increasingly challenging in the future.

Appendix

Agreements and Laws Protecting Humpback Whales

INTERNATIONAL

The International Whaling Commission (IWC)

The IWC was established in 1946 with the purpose of providing "the proper conservation of whale stocks, and thus make possible the orderly development of the whaling industry." As is clearly stated, conservation is only part of its mandate — and this is for the purpose of continued whaling. However, the IWC is the only international management forum for whales — it is the organization that officially protected humpback whales and other species, designated sanctuaries, and set whaling limits and seasons. There are seventy-seven member nations. Critically, no government is bound by any IWC regulation if it chooses to object.

Convention on International Trade in Endangered Species of Wild Fauna and Flora (CITES)

CITES is a 1975 international agreement between governments whose purpose is to ensure that international trade in specimens of wild animals and plants does not threaten their survival. It accords varying degrees of protection to more than 30,000 species of animals and plants. Humpback whales are one of these species. The way it works is that, if one country flaunts international agreement not to hunt the whales, they cannot sell the products legally to another country. There are currently 172 countries that are members, but similar to the IWC, adherence to the agreement is voluntary. Each member country adopts its own domestic legislation to ensure that CITES is implemented at the national level.

NATIONAL

In US Waters

Marine Mammal Protection Act (MMPA) 1972

All marine mammals are protected under the MMPA. The MMPA prohibits, with certain exceptions, the take of marine mammals in US waters and by US citizens on the high seas, and the importation of marine mammals and marine mammal products into the US.

Endangered Species Act (ESA) 1973

The Endangered Species Act provides for the conservation of species that are endangered or threatened throughout all or a significant portion of their range, and the conservation of the ecosystems on which they depend.

A species is considered *endangered* if it is in danger of extinction throughout all or a significant portion of its range. A species is considered *threatened* if it is likely to become an endangered species within the foreseeable future.

The definition of *take* (which in turn defines what these Acts mean to whales) is slightly different between the two Acts.

- *Take* under the MMPA means to "harass, hunt, capture, kill or collect, or attempt to harass, hunt, capture, kill or collect."

- *Take* under the ESA means "to harass, harm, pursue, hunt, shoot, wound, kill, trap, capture, or collect, or to attempt to engage in any such conduct."

Special permits are required to potentially "take," that is, "harass," whales during research operations. As regards research, any disturbance that changes natural behavior (however slightly) is considered a "take."

Hawaii State Regulations

The Hawaii State Department of Land and Natural Resources (DLNR) manages aquatic species in Hawaiian waters, including humpback whales. They work in collaboration with federal departments in enforcing Hawaiian humpback whale protection regulations, and require state permits (in addition to the Federal NMFS permits) for any activity that may contravene the regulations.

In Canadian Waters

Humpback whales seen in Hawaii in the winter may spend the summer feeding season in waters under Canadian jurisdiction, along the British Columbia coastline.

Cetacean Protection Regulations (1982)

Cetacean Protection Regulations, issued under the Fisheries Act, require that anyone, other than Indians and Inuit, wishing to hunt cetaceans must obtain a license from the Minister of Fisheries before doing so. Indians and Inuit are allowed to hunt all cetaceans, except "right whales" (balaenids), without a license if the products are used for local consumption.

The Cetacean Protection Regulations prohibit any form of harassment of cetaceans, including repeated attempts to pursue, disperse, herd whales and any repeated intentional act or negligence resulting in the disruption of their normal behavior.

Species at Risk Act (SARA) 2003

This Act provides for further protection of species considered at risk. Currently North Pacific humpback whales are categorized as "threatened" under this Act.

Among other things, this Act makes it an offence to kill, harm, harass, capture, or take an individual that is extirpated, endangered, or threatened; possess, collect, buy, sell, or trade an individual of a listed species or its part or derivative; damage or destroy the residence of one or more individuals of a listed species.

When Hawaiian Humpbacks
Are Not in US or Canadian Waters

Hawaiian humpback whales migrate through, and range into, international waters as well as the national waters of other North Pacific Rim countries. Protection in these waters relies on agreements (nonbinding) made at the IWC and CITES as discussed above.

Glossary

agonistic All aspects of aggression, including threats and actual attack, appeasement, and flight.

allomaternal Care-giving of an infant by an animal other than its mother.

anecdote A short personal account of an incident or event.

artiodactyls An order of mammals, the even-toed ungulates (hoofed animals), that includes cows, sheep, and antelope. They share a common evolutionary ancestor with whales.

baleen whales Whales that, instead of teeth, have a filtering system in their mouth made out of keratin plates called baleen.

birth rate Average number of offspring produced by a female over a given time.

blowhole Nostrils of a whale through which they inhale and exhale. Baleen whales have two blowholes side by side — toothed whales have only one.

breach *See Actions and Postures*

breath-holders Whale research jargon usually referring to a pair of adult whales that spend long periods underwater and little time on the surface.

bubblestream *See Actions and Postures*

cetaceans The order of mammals that includes whales, dolphins, and porpoises.

CITES Convention on International Trade in Endangered Species of Wild Fauna and Flora, an international agreement to prevent countries trading in products of endangered species.

competitive behavior Interactions between animals striving for the same, mutually exclusive, goal.

conservation The protection of living plants and animals and their habitats.

cooperative behavior Behavior involving individuals working together (helping each other) towards a goal.

copepod Small (mostly planktonic) animals that are a major source of protein in oceans and important to whales both directly as prey and as a critical component of marine food webs.

Cousteau, Jacques French filmmaker who popularized ocean exploration and conservation through his TV programs in the 1960s and 70s.

cumulative effects A number of small impacts that combine to create a greater impact.

diatom Unicellular (one-celled) algae (phytoplankton) that are the basis of many marine food webs.

Discovery tag Metal dart once shot into a living whale to be recovered at time of death (from whaling) to determine its movements.

dominance hierarchy Social hierarchy (in animals often determined by physical differences) where certain individuals control the distribution of available resources (e.g. receptive females).

down-list The reassignment of a species from a higher to a lower category of protection (e.g. from "endangered" to "threatened," or from "threatened" to "recovered").

echolocation A method in which an animal emits pulses of sound and listens to the echoes to determine location, range, and nature of objects in the environment for navigation and feeding.

epimeletic Helping behavior; in cetaceans it often involves healthy individual(s) helping sick or injured ones.

escort An adult male humpback whale that accompanies a mother with calf, and that will defend his position against other males.

estrus The period when a female is sexually receptive, when eggs are produced and, with mating, pregnancy is most likely to occur.

extant A species or group of organisms that still exists, that is not extinct.

extinct A species or group of organisms that no longer exists.

Feresa (Pygmy Killer Whale) A slender black dolphin with distinctive white lips less than ten feet (3 m) in length, widely distributed in tropical waters.

fertilization The fusion of sperm and egg that leads to an embryo (and offspring).

fitness In biology, the ability of an organism to transfer its genes to the next generation.

flipper Fin on the forward sides of the whale; in humpbacks they are long and wing-like.

gene Fundamental unit that contains genetic information determining the characteristics of a living organism.

genetic diversity The range of genes within a species.

gestation The development of the embryo in mammals. The gestation period is the time between fertilization of the egg and birth.

GPS Standard short form of Global Positioning System, which provides exact longitude and latitude position determined by satellite.

Greenpeace One of the first grassroots organizations to protest whaling in the 1970s.

habitat A part of the environment that is occupied by a specific plant or animal species.

headknobs Distinctive knobs on the top of the head of humpback whales (formally called tubercules). Each knob has a hair in it that may have a sensory function.

herring A small fish (< 15 in/40 cm) that lives in vast schools in oceans of the northern hemisphere; it is an important prey for whales.

hydrophone An underwater microphone (used to detect whale sounds).

hypothesis A potential explanation based on observations of a phenomenon or behavior that is not yet fully understood.

IWC The International Whaling Commission, an international organization that manages whaling and therefore influences whale conservation.

joiner A common research term for a lone adult whale (male) that joins a singing humpback whale.

juvenile A young whale that has separated from its mother but is not yet sexually mature.

killer whale (*Orcinus orca*) Largest of the dolphin family (15–30 ft, or 5–10 m). Found in all oceans; top oceanic predator that may include large whales in its diet.

krill A small, shrimp-like marine animal (a type of zooplankton called a euphausiid) that is an important food source for some baleen whales.

lactation Production of milk from the mammary glands by the adult female mammal in order to suckle its young.

lee The side sheltered from the wind, usually due to high land acting as a windbreak.

lek Gathering of males for purposes of competitive mating display.

mammary glands Glands in female mammals that produce milk for suckling young.

migration Cyclical movements that occur during the life of an animal at definite intervals. In humpback whales, migration occurs between summer feeding and winter breeding grounds.

Mysticeti The sub-order of cetaceans that includes the baleen whales.

non-agonistic Used to refer to behavior patterns that are not aggressive in nature.

nursery Specific location where young animals are found.

Odontoceti The sub-order of cetaceans that includes the toothed whales.

operational sex ratio Ratio of number of mature males to number of sexually receptive females available at any given time during the breeding season.

ovaries That part of the female reproductive system that produces eggs.

ovulation The release of the egg from the ovary into the oviduct, where it may be fertilized.

peduncle Area of a whale's body just forward of the tail (also referred to as the tail stock).

photogrammetry Photographic technique to determine the size of an object.

photo-identification (photo-ID) Identification of individual animals by photographs of natural markings.

photo-ID matches Repeat sightings of the same individual whale determined by matching identification photographs taken at different times.

placenta Point of attachment of embryo to mother and through which the embryo is nourished.

population Total individuals of one species that inhabit a particular locality or region.

post-partum estrus Estrus that occurs shortly after giving birth.

Pseudorca (False Killer Whale) Black dolphin up to about fifteen feet (5 m) in length, widely distributed in warm temperate waters and tropical waters. Potential predator of humpback whales.

reproductive strategy Life history or behavior that results in greater survival and reproductive success.

sardine A small fish (also known as a pilchard) living in huge schools and an important food to whales.

satellite tag Electronic tag attached to a whale that sends location signals to a satellite to allow tracking over extended times and distances.

scientific process Testing a hypothesis by means of experiments designed to either support or invalidate it.

seasonally polyestrus A term used to describe a female that has multiple estrus cycles during a specific time of year.

sexual maturity Age when an individual animal can reproduce.

social sounds Sounds made by humpback whales that are not song, that is, not repeated in a cyclical pattern.

song In biology, a series of sounds that are repeated over and over. Humpback whale males sing a complex, ever-changing song.

spermatogenesis Sperm production in the male.

SPLASH Acronym for a study on the abundance and status of North Pacific humpback whales from 2004 to 2006, termed Structure of Population Levels of Abundance and Status of Humpback Whales.

sub-population A portion of the entire population often defined by a particular characteristic (e.g. all juvenile humpbacks in Hawaii).

surface active group (SAG) (or competitive group) An often fast-moving group of multiple males and one female characterized by competition between the males over access to the female.

tail fluke Each side of a whale's tail.

tail stock Area of a whale's body just forward of the tail, also called a peduncle.

testes That part of the male reproductive system that produces sperm.

throat pleats Pleats in the underside of a whale's throat that allow the throat to greatly expand when taking in mouthfuls of food or in displays.

tiger shark A large predatory shark (to 14 ft, or 4.25 m) common around islands in the central Pacific; it eats almost anything.

toothed whale A whale with teeth, including the sperm whale, killer whales, and all dolphins and porpoises (sub-order Odontoceti).

zooplankton Small animals that float in ocean currents; they are a major food source for baleen whales.

Actions and Postures

Humpback whales engage in specific actions and postures while involved in the behavior patterns described in this book. In many cases, several different terms are used to describe the same activity, as different research groups coined the terms. Below, the most common term is listed first with alternatives in parentheses.

The actions and postures that occur in a variety of social situations, by both sexes (or sex specificity not confirmed), and throughout the year, are described first. Other activities, primarily (but not exclusively) performed by males when competing for females are presented separately below.

Occur in a Variety of Social Situations

Side Fluke (*half fluke, lateral fluke display*)
Whale is at the water surface with one fluke blade extended above the surface as it swims on its side.

Inverted Posture (*belly-up*)
Whale turns ventral side towards the surface.

Roll
The whale rolls ventral side or belly-up, at times slapping flippers on the surface as it rolls all the way over.

Head Rise (*spy hop*)
Whale raises its head vertically out of the water while stationary with flippers outstretched (without open mouth or extended throat pleats).

Tail Extension
Whale raises its tail slowly into the air, usually high enough that the genital area is above the surface, and holds it there for a time.

Tail Arch
The whale arches and curves its tail stock and fluke into an "S" shape on the horizontal plane and holds it there while swimming forward.

Flippering *(flipper slap)*
The whale raises a flipper into the air and slaps it down on the water surface once or many (20+) times in succession.

Tail Lob *(lob tail, fluke slap)*
The whale slaps its tail on the surface, either right-way-up (slapping the underside of its flukes) or belly-up (slapping dorsal surface of its flukes).

Rear Body Throw *(tail throw, peduncle slap)*
The whale throws the rear portion of its body from the water, often twisting to land on its side.

Belly-Flop *(half breach)*
The whale leaps partially out of the water and lands on its belly.

Breach
The whale leaps from the water, spinning in the air before re-entry. Two associated whales may breach simultaneously (double breach).

Occur Primarily in Competitive Groups of Males

Tail Lash *(fluke swish)*
One whale lashes its tail, often towards another. Can occur with flukes on a horizontal or vertical plane.

Head Lunge
The whale lunges forward with most of its head coming out of the water.

Underwater Blow
The whale releases a blast of air from its blowhole below the surface of the water, often just prior to surfacing.

Bubblestream *(bubble trail)*
The submerged whale releases a controlled stream of bubbles from its blowhole, leaving a trail behind it.

Air Gulp *(throat inflation)*
The whale gulps air, greatly extending its throat pleats. It releases the air underwater.

Head Slap *(chin slap)*
Whale lunges/leaps partially out of the water and strikes the ventral side of its head forcefully on the surface.

Head Lift
The whale swims with its back arched and head above the surface.

Jaw Clap
The whale opens and closes its jaws, clapping them together, at times audibly.

Chasing *(tail chasing)*
One whale rapidly chases another. The leader may throw its tail upward with the chaser lunging behind.

Charge
One whale charges at another, often bubblestreaming in the process.

Block
One whale blocks the path of another with its body.

Strike
One whale intentionally strikes another with its flukes, whether underwater or on the surface.

Collision
Two whales collide, apparently intentionally.

Trumpeting
A whale vocalizes on the surface with a prolonged, low, foghorn-like sound emitted from the blowhole.

213

References

Amos, W. 1997. Marine mammal tissue sample collection and preservation for genetic analysis. In *Molecular genetics of marine mammals*. eds. A. Dizon, S. Chivers, and W. Perrin, 107–116. Lawrence, KS: The Society for Marine Mammalogy.

Au, W. W., L. J. Mobley, W. C. Burgess, M. O. Lammers, and P. E. Nachtigall. 2000. Seasonal and diurnal trends of chorusing humpback whales wintering in waters off western Maui. *Marine Mammal Science* 16:530–544.

Baker, C. S. 1985. The population structure and social organization of humpback whales (*Megaptera novaeangliae*) in the central and eastern North Pacific. PhD diss., Univ. of Hawaii, Honolulu.

Baker, C. S., and L. M. Herman. 1981. Migration and local movement of humpback whales in Hawaiian waters. *Canadian Journal of Zoology* 59:460–469.

———. 1984. Aggressive behavior between humpback whales (*Megaptera novaeangliae*) wintering in Hawaiian waters. *Canadian Journal of Zoology* 62:1922–1937.

———. 1984. Seasonal contrasts in the social behavior of the humpback whale. *Cetus* 5:14–16.

———. 1987. Alternative population estimates of humpback whales (*Megaptera novaeangliae*) in Hawaiian waters. *Canadian Journal of Zoology* 65:2818–2821.

Baker, C. S., L. M. Herman, A. Perry, W. S. Lawton, J. M. Straley, A. A. Wolman, G. D. Kaufman, H. E. Winn, J. D. Hall, J. M. Reinke, and J. Ostman. 1986. Migratory movement and population structure of humpback whales (*Megaptera novaeangliae*) in the central and eastern North Pacific. *Marine Ecology Progress Series* 31:105–119.

Baker, C. S., A. Perry, and L. M. Herman. 1987. Reproductive histories of female humpback whales, *Megaptera novaeangliae*, in the North Pacific. *Marine Ecology Progress Series* 41:103–114.

Barlow, J. 2006. Cetacean abundance in Hawaiian waters estimated from a summer/fall survey in 2002. *Marine Mammal Science* 22:446–464.

Barlow, J., and P. J. Clapham. 1996. A new birth interval approach to estimating demographic parameters of humpback whales. *Ecology* 78:535–545.

Bauer, G. H. 1986. The behavior of humpback whales in Hawaii and modification of behavior induced by human intervention. PhD diss., Univ. of Hawaii, Honolulu.

Bermuda Zoological Society. 1983. Frank Watlington. *Newsletter of the Bermuda Zoological Society* 6:1 & 5.

Best, P. B., J. L. Bannister, R. L. Brownell, and G. P. Donovan, eds. 2001. Right whales: Worldwide status. Special Issue 2, *Cetacean Research and Management*.

Bigg, M. A., I. B. MacAskie, and G. Ellis. 1976. *Abundance and movement of killer whales off eastern and southern Vancouver Island with comments on management*. Unpublished report. Nanaimo, BC: Pacific Biological Station. Canada.

Brown, M., and P. Corkeron. 1995. Pod characteristics of migrating humpback whales (*Megaptera novaeangliae*) off the east Australian coast. *Behavior* 132:163–179.

Brown, M. R., P. J. Corkeron, P. T. Hale, K. W. Schultz, and M. M. Bryden. 1995. Evidence for a sex segregated migration in the humpback whale (*Megaptera novaeangliae*). *Proceedings Royal Society London Series* B 259:229–234.

Calambokidis, J., E. A. Falcone, T. J. Quinn, A. M. Burdin, P. J. Clapham, J. K. F. Ford, C. M. Gabriele, R. LeDuc, D. Mattila, L. Rojas-Bracho, J. M. Straley, B. Taylor, J. Urban, D. Weller, B. H. Witteveen, M. Yamaguchi, A. Bendlin, D. Camacho, K. Flynn, A. Havron, J. Huggins, and N. Maloney. 2008. SPLASH: Structure of Population Levels of Abundance and Status of Humpback Whales in the North Pacific. Final Report U.S. Dept. of Commerce Contract AB133F-03-RP-00078 Seattle, WA: Cascadia Research, Olympia, WA.

Calambokidis, J., G. H. Steiger, J. M. Straley, L. M. Herman, S. Cerchio, D. R. Salden, J. Urban R., J. K. Jacobsen, O. von Zeigesar, K. C. Balcomb, C. M. Gabriele, M. E. Dahlheim, S. Uchida, G. Ellis, Y. Mitamura, P. Ladron de Guevara, M. Yamaguchi, F. Sato, S. A. Mizroch, L. Schlender, K. Rasmussen, J. Barlow, and T. J. Quinn II. 2001. Movements and population structure of humpback whales in the North Pacific. *Marine Mammal Science* 17:769–794.

Calambokidis, J., G. H. Steiger, J. M. Straley, T. J. Quinn II, L. M. Herman, S. Cerchio, D. R. Salden, M. Yamaguchi, F. Sato, J. Urban, J. Jacobsen, O. von Ziegesar, K. C. Balcomb, C. M. Gabriele, M. E. Dahlheim, N. Higashi, S. Uchida, J. K. B. Ford, Y. Miyamura, P. Ladron de Guevara, S. A. Mizroch, L. Schlender, and K. Rasmussen. 1997. *Abundance and population structure of humpback whales in the North Pacific basin*. Contract No. 50ABNF500113, Southwest Fisheries Science Center, La Jolla, CA .

Cartwright, R. 1999. Factors affecting the behavior of humpback whale, *Megaptera novaeangliae*, calves whilst in Hawaiian waters. MS thesis, Manchester Metropolitan Univ., UK.

———. 2005. A comparative study of the behaviour and dynamics of humpback whale (*Megaptera novaeangliae*) mother and calf pairs during their residence in nursery waters. PhD diss., Manchester Metropolitan Univ., UK.

Cerchio, S. 1998. Estimates of humpback whale abundance off Kauai, 1989–1993: Evaluating biases associated with sampling the Hawaiian Islands breeding assemblage. *Marine Ecology Progress Series* 175:23–34.

Cerchio, S., C. Gabriele, T. F. Norris, and L. M. Herman. 1998. Movements of humpback whales between Kauai and Hawaii: Implication for the population structure and abundance estimation in the Hawaiian Islands. *Marine Ecology Progress Series*, 175:13–22.

Cerchio, S., J. K. Jacobsen, D. M. Cholewiak, E. A. Falcone, and D. A. Merriwether. 2005. Paternity in humpback whales, *Megaptera novaeangliae*: Assessing polygyny and skew in male reproductive success. *Animal Behavior* 70:267–277.

Cerchio, S., J. K. Jacobsen, and T. F. Norris. 2001. Temporal and geographic variation in songs of humpback whales (*Megaptera novaeangliae*): Synchronous change in Hawaiian and Mexican breeding assemblages. *Animal Behavior* 62:313–329.

Chadwick, D. H. 2007. What are they doing down there? *National Geographic* Magazine Jan. 2007:72–93.

Chittleborough, R. G. 1953. Aerial observations on the humpback whale *M. nodosa*. *Australian Journal of Marine and Freshwater Research* 9:1–18.

———. 1958. The breeding cycle of the female humpback whale *Megaptera nodosa* (Bonaterre). *Australian Journal of Marine and Freshwater Research* 9:1–18.

———. 1965. Dynamics of two populations of the humpback whale *Megaptera novaeangliae* (Borowski). *Australian Journal of Marine and Freshwater Research* 16:33–128.

Chu, K. C. 1988. Dive times and ventilation patterns of singing humpback whales (*Megaptera novaeangliae*). *Canadian Journal of Zoology* 66:1322–1327.

Chu, K. C., and P. Harcourt. 1986. Behavioral correlations with aberrant patterns in humpback whale songs. *Behavioral Ecology and Sociobiology* 19:309–312.

Clapham. P. J. 1992. Age of attainment of sexual maturity in humpback whales, *Megaptera novaeangliae*. *Canadian Journal of Zoology* 70:1470–1472.

———. 1993. The social and reproductive biology of North Atlantic humpback whales, *Megaptera novaeangliae*. PhD diss., Univ. of Aberdeen, Scotland.

———. 1996. The social and reproductive biology of humpback whales: An ecological perspective. *Mammal Review* 26:27–49.

———. 2002. Humpback whales. In *Encyclopedia of marine mammals*, eds. W. F. Perrin, B. Wursig, and J. G. M. Thewissen, 589–592. New York: Academic Press.

Clapham, P. J., and D. K. Mattila. 1990. Humpback whale songs as indications of migration routes. *Marine Mammal Science* 6:155–160.

Clapham, P. J., and C. A. Mayo. 1987. Reproduction and recruitment of individually identified humpback whales, *Megaptera novaeangliae*, observed in Massachusetts Bay, 1979–1985. *Canadian Journal of Zoology* 65:2853–2863.

———. 1990. Reproduction of humpback whales, *Megaptera novaeangliae*, observed in the Gulf of Maine. Special Issue, *Reports of the International Whaling Commission*, 12:171–175.

Clapham, P. J., P. J. Palsboll, D. K. Mattila, and V. Oswaldo. 1992. Composition of humpback whale competitive groups in the West Indies. *Behavior* 122:182–194.

Clapham, P. J., S. B. Young, and R. L. Brownell, Jr. 1999. Baleen whales: Conservation issues and the status of the most endangered populations. *Mammal Review* 29:35–60.

Clark, C. W., and P. J. Clapham. 2004. Acoustic monitoring of a humpback whale (*Megaptera novaeangliae*) feeding ground shows continual singing into late spring. *Proceedings Royal Society of London* 271:1051–1057.

Clutton-Brock, T. H. 1989. Mammalian mating systems. *Proceedings Royal Society of London* B 236:339–372.

Committee on Abrupt Climate Change and National Research Council. 2002. Abrupt climate change: Inevitable surprises. Washington, DC: *National Academy Press*.

Craig, A. S., and L. M. Herman. 1997. Sex differences in site fidelity and migration of humpback whales (*Megaptera novaeangliae*) to the Hawaiian Islands. *Canadian Journal of Zoology* 75:1923–1933.

———. 2000. Habitat preferences of female humpback whales, *Megaptera novaeangliae*, in the Hawaiian Islands are associated with reproductive status. *Marine Ecology Progress Series* 193:209–216.

Craig, A. S., L. M. Herman, C. M. Gabriele, and A. A. Pack. 2003. Migratory timing of humpback whales (*Megaptera novaeangliae*) in central North Pacific varies with age, sex and reproductive status. *Behavior* 140:981–1001.

Craig, A. S., L. M. Herman, and A. A. Pack. 2002. Male mate choice and male-male competition coexist in the humpback whale (*Megaptera novaeangliae*). *Canadian Journal of Zoology* 80:745–755.

———. 1983. Migrations, abundance and behavior of Hawaiian humpback whales (*Megaptera novaeangliae*). PhD diss., Univ. of California, Santa Cruz, CA.

———. 1984. Gray whales off Vancouver Island, British Columbia. In *The gray whale*, eds. M. L. Jones, S. Leatherwood, and S. Swartz, 267–287. New York: Academic Press.

Darling, J. D. 1990. *With the whales*. Minocqua, WI: Northword Press.

Darling, J. D., and M. Bérubé. 2001. Interactions of singing humpback whales with other males. *Marine Mammal Science* 17:570–584.

Darling, J. D., and S. Cerchio. 1993. Movement of a humpback whale between Japan and Hawaii. *Marine Mammal Science* 9:84–89.

Darling, J. D., and C. M. Jurasz. 1983. Migratory destinations of North Pacific humpback whales (*Megaptera novaeangliae*). In *Communication and behavior of whales*. AAAS Selected Symposia Series. ed. R. Payne, 359–368. Boulder, CO: Westview Press.

Darling, J. D., K. M. Gibson, and G. Silber. 1983. Observations on the abundance and behavior of humpback whales (*Megaptera novaeangliae*) off West Maui, Hawaii 1977–79. In *Communication and behavior of whales*. AAAS Selected Symposia Series. ed. R. Payne, 201–222. Boulder, CO: Westview Press.

Darling, J. D., M. E. Jones, and C. P. Nicklin. 2006. Humpback whale songs: Do they organize males during the breeding season? *Behavior* 143:1051–1101.

Darling, J. D., and D. J. McSweeney. 1985. Observations on the migrations of North Pacific humpback whales (*Megaptera novaeangliae*). *Canadian Journal of Zoology* 63:308–314.

Darling, J. D., and H. Morowitz. 1986. Census of "Hawaiian" humpback whales (*Megaptera novaeangliae*) by individual identification. *Canadian Journal of Zoology* 64:105–111.

Dawbin, W. H. 1966. The seasonal migratory cycle of humpback whales. In *Whales, dolphins and porpoises*. ed. K. S. Norris, 145–170. Berkeley: Univ. of California Press.

De Guise, S., D. Martineau, P. Beland, and P. Fournier. 1995. Possible mechanisms of action of environmental contaminants on St. Lawrence beluga whales (*Delphinapterus leucas*). *Environmental Health Perspectives* 103:73–77.

Dietz, T. 1982. *Tales of whales*. Portland, ME: Gannett Publishing Co.

Doroshenko, N. V. 2000. Soviet catches of humpback whales (*Megaptera novaeagliae*) in the North Pacific. In *Soviet whaling data* (1949–1979), 48–93. Moscow: Center for Russian Environmental Policy, Marine Mammal Council.

Elliott, W., and M. Simmonds. 2007. Whales in hot water? The impact of a changing climate on whales, dolphins and porpoises: A call for action. Chippenham, UK: WWF-International, Gland, Switzerland / WDCS.

Ellis, R. 1991. *Men and whales*. New York: Alfred A. Knopf.

Emlen, S. T., and L. W. Oring. 1977. Ecology, sexual selection, and the evolution of mating systems. *Science* 197:215–223.

Frankel, A. S., C. W. Clark, L. M. Herman, and C. Gabriele. 1995. Spatial distribution, habitat utilization, and social interactions of humpback whales, *Megaptera novaeangliae*, of Hawaii determined using acoustic and visual techniques. *Canadian Journal of Zoology* 73:1134–1146.

Frazer, L. N., and E. Mercado. 2000. A sonar model for the humpback whale song. *Journal of Oceanic Engineering* 25:160–181.

Gabriele, C. M. 1992. The behavior and residence characteristics of reproductive classes of humpback whales (*Megaptera novaeangliae*) in the Hawaiian Islands. MA thesis. Univ. of Hawaii, Honolulu, HI.

Gabriele, C. M., J. M. Straley, L. M. Herman, and R. J. Coleman. 1996. Fastest documented migration of a North Pacific humpback whale. *Marine Mammal Science* 12:457–464.

Gabriele, C. M., J. M. Straley, and J. L. Neilson. 2007. Age at first calving of female humpback whales in southeastern Alaska. *Marine Mammal Science* 23:226–239.

Glockner, D. A. 1983. Determining the sex of humpback whales (*Megaptera novaeangliae*) in their natural environment. In *Communication and behavior of whales*, ed. R. Payne, 447–464. AAAS Selected Symposia Series. Boulder, CO: Westview Press.

Glockner, D. A., and S. Venus. 1983. Identification, growth rate, and behavior of humpback whale (*Megaptera novaeangliae*) cows and calves in the waters off Maui, Hawaii 1977–79. In *Communication and behavior of whales*, ed. R. Payne, 223–258. AAAS Selected Symposia Series. Boulder, CO: Westview Press.

Glockner-Ferrari, D. A., and M. J. Ferrari. 1984. Reproduction in humpback whales, *Megaptera novaeangliae*, in Hawaiian waters. Special Issue, *Reports of the International Whaling Commission* 6:237–242.

———. 1985. Individual identification, behavior, reproduction and distribution of humpback whales, *Megaptera novaeangliae*, in Hawaii. Final Report U.S. Marine Mammal Commission, Contract MM2629752-5. Washington, DC: U.S. Marine Mammal Commission.

———. 1990. Reproduction in the humpback whale (*Megaptera novaeangliae*) in Hawaiian waters, 1975–1988: The life history, reproductive rates, and behavior of known individuals identified through surface and underwater photography. Special Issue, *Reports of the International Whaling Commission* 12:161–167.

Helweg, D. A. 1989. The daily and seasonal patterns of behavior and abundance of humpback whales (*Megaptera novaeangliae*) in Hawaiian waters. MA thesis, Univ. of Hawaii, Honolulu, HI.

Helweg, D. A., A. S. Frankel, F. R. Mobley, and L. M. Herman. 1992. Humpback whale song: Our current understanding. In *Marine Mammal Sensory Systems*, eds. J. Thomas et al., 459–483. New York: Plenum Press.

Helweg, D. A., and L. M. Herman. 1994. Diurnal patterns of behavior and group membership of humpback whales (*Megaptera novaeangliae*) wintering in Hawaiian waters. *Ethology* 98:298–311.

Herman, L. M. 1979. Humpback whales in Hawaiian waters: A study in historical ecology. *Pacific Search* 33:1–15.

Herman, L. M., and R. C. Antinoja. 1977. Humpback whales in the Hawaiian breeding waters: Population and pod characteristics. *Scientific Reports Whales Research Institute Tokyo* 29:59–85.

Herman, L. M., and W. N. Tavolga. 1980. The communications systems of cetaceans. In *Cetacean behavior, mechanisms and functions*, ed. L. M. Herman, 149–209. New York: John Wiley and Sons.

Hoyt, E. 2001. Whale watching 2001: Worldwide tourism numbers, expenditures, and expanding socioeconomic benefits. Yarmouth Port, MA: International Fund for Animal Welfare.

Jaquet, N. 2006. A simple photogrammetric technique to measure sperm whales at sea. *Marine Mammal Science* 22:862–879.

Jones, M. L., and S. L. Swartz. 1984. Demography and phenology of gray whales and evaluation of whale-watching activities in Laguna San Ignacio, Baja California sur, Mexico. In *The gray whale*, eds. M. L. Jones, S. J. Leatherwood, and S. L. Swartz, 289–307. New York: Academic Press.

Katona, S., B. Baxter, O. Brazier, S. Kraus, J. Perkins, and H. Whitehead. 1979. Identification of humpback whales by fluke photographs. *In Behavior of marine animals — current perspectives in research, Vol. 3: Cetaceans.* eds. H. E. Winn and B. L. Olla, 33–44. Plenum Press, N.Y.

Kellogg, R. 1928. What is known of the migrations of some of the whalebone whales. *Annual Reports Smithsonian Institution* 1928:467–494.

Krebs, J. R., and Davies, N. B. 1996. *Introduction to behavioral ecology.* Oxford, UK: Blackwell Scientific.

Lindbergh, J. 1967. Underwater is the right place to meet a whale. *Life* magazine December 1967:50–51.

Lockyer, C. 1981. Growth and energy budgets of large baleen whales from the southern hemisphere. In *Mammals in the seas*, Vol 3. 379–487. Rome: Food and Agricultural Organization of the United Nations.

Lockyer, C. 1984. Review of baleen whale (Mysticeti) reproduction and implications for management. Special Issue, *Reports of the International Whaling Commission* 6:27–48.

Lyman, E., and D. Mattila. 2007. *Summary of 2007 disentanglement season. Hawaiian Islands disentanglement network report.* Kihei, HI: Hawaiian Islands Humpback Whale National Marine Sanctuary.

Lyman, E., and D. Mattila. 2008. *Summary of 2007/2008 large whale entanglement and ship strike reports. Hawaiian Islands disentanglement network report.* Kihei, HI: Hawaiian Islands Humpback Whale National Marine Sanctuary.

Mate, B. R., R. Gisiner, and J. Mobley. 1998. Local and migratory movements of the Hawaiian humpback whales tracked by satellite telemetry. *Canadian Journal of Zoology* 76:863–868.

Mate, B. R., R. Mesecar, and B. Lagerquist. 2007. The evolution of satellite-monitored radio tags for large whales: One laboratory's experience. *Deep-Sea Research* II 54:224–247.

Matthews, L. H. 1937. The humpback whale, *Megaptera nodosa. Discovery Reports* 17:7–92.

Mattila, D. K., P. J. Clapham, S. K. Katona, and G. S. Stone. 1989. Population composition of humpback whales, *Megaptera novaeangliae*, on Silver Bank 1984. *Canadian Journal of Zoology* 67:281–285.

Mattila, D. K., L. N. Guinee, and C. A. Mayo. 1987. Humpback whale songs on a North Atlantic feeding ground. *Journal of Mammalogy* 68:880–883.

McSweeney, D. J., R. W. Baird, and S. D. Mahaffy. 2007. Site fidelity, associations and movements of Curvier's (*Ziphius cavirostris*) and Blainville's (*Mesoplodon densirostris*) beaked whales off the Island of Hawaii. *Marine Mammal Science* 23:666–687.

McSweeney, D. J., K. C. Chu, W. F. Dolphin, and L. N. Guinee. 1989. North Pacific humpback whale songs: A comparison of southeast Alaskan feeding ground songs and Hawaiian wintering ground songs. *Marine Mammal Science* 5:16–138.

Mead, J. G., and J. D. Gold. 2002. *Whales and dolphins in question. The Smithsonian answer book*. Washington, DC: Smithsonian Institution Press.

Medrano, L., M. Salinas, I. Salas, P. Ladron de Guevara, A. Aguayo, J. Jacobsen, and C. S. Baker. 1994. Sex identification of humpback whales, *Megaptera novaeangliae*, on the wintering grounds of the Mexican Pacific Ocean. *Canadian Journal of Zoology* 72:1771–1774.

Mesnick, S. 1997. Sexual alliances: Evidence and evolutionary implications. In *Feminism and evolutionary biology: Boundaries, intersections and frontiers*, ed. P. A. Gowaty, 207–257. New York: Chapman & Hall.

Mikhalev, Y. A. 2000. Biological characteristics of humpbacks taken in the Antarctic Area V by the whaling fleets Slava and Sovietskaya Ukraina. Paper IA12 submitted to the Scientific Committee of the International Whaling Commission (Unpublished, cited in Noad and Cato 2007).

Miller, P. J. O., N. Biassoni, A. Samuels, and P. L. Tyack. 2000. Whale songs lengthen in response to sonar. *Nature* 405:203.

Mobley, J. R., and L. M. Herman. 1985. Transience of social affiliations among humpback whales (*Megaptera novaeangliae*) on Hawaiian wintering grounds. *Canadian Journal of Zoology* 63:762–772.

Mobley, J. R., G. B. Bauer, and L. M. Herman. 1999. Changes over a ten-year interval in the distribution and relative abundance of humpback whales (*Megaptera novaeangliae*) wintering in Hawaiian waters. *Aquatic Mammals* 25:63–72.

Mobley, J. R., P. H. Forestall, and R. Grotefendt. 1994. Results of aerial surveys in Hawaiian waters. Annual report. Arlington, VA: Advanced Research Projects Agency.

Mobley, J. R., L. M. Herman, and A. S. Frankel. 1988. Responses of wintering humpback whales (*Megaptera novaeangliae*) to playbacks of winter and summer vocalizations and of synthetic sound. *Behavioral Ecology and Sociobiology* 23:211–223.

Nishiwaki, M. 1959. Humpback whales in Ryukyuan waters. *Scientific Reports of the Whales Research Institute Tokyo* 14:49–86.

———. 1960. Ryukyuan humpback whaling in 1960. *Scientific Reports of the Whales Research Institute Tokyo* 15:1–16.

————. 1962. Ryukyuan whaling in 1961. *Scientific Reports of the Whales Research Institute Tokyo* 16:19–28.

————. 1966. Distribution and migration of the larger cetaceans in the North Pacific as shown by Japanese whaling results. In *Whales, dolphins and porpoises*, ed. K. S. Norris, 171–191. Berkeley, CA: Univ. of California Press.

Noad, M. J., and D. H. Cato. 2007. Swimming speeds of singing and non-singing humpback whales during migration. *Marine Mammal Science* 23:481–495.

Noad, M. J., D. H. Cato, M. M. Bryden, M. N. Jenner, and C. S. Jenner. 2000. Cultural revolution in whale songs. *Nature* 408:537.

Pack, A. A., L. M. Herman, A. S. Craig, S. S. Spitz, and M. H. Deakos. 2002. Penis extrusions by humpback whales (*Megaptera novaeangliae*). *Aquatic Mammals* 28:131–146.

Pack, A. A., D. Salden, M. J Ferrari, D. A. Glockner-Ferrari, L. M. Herman, H. A. Stubbs, and J. M. Straley. 1998. Male humpback whale dies in competitive group. *Marine Mammal Science* 14:861–873.

Palsboll, P. 1999. Genetic tagging: Contemporary molecular ecology. *Biological Journal of the Linnean Society* 68:3–22.

Payne, R. S., and L. N. Guinee. 1983. Humpback whale songs as an indicator of "stocks." In *Communication and behavior of whales*. AAAS Selected Symposia Series, ed. R. Payne, 333–358. Boulder, CO: Westview Press.

Payne, R., and S. McVay. 1971. Songs of humpback whales. *Science* 173:585–597.

Payne, K. P., and R. S. Payne. 1985. Large scale changes over 19 years in songs of humpback whales off Bermuda. *Zeitschrift für Tierpsychologie* 68:89–114.

Payne, R., O. Brazier, E. M. Dorsey, J. S. Perkins, V. J. Rowntree, and A. Titus. 1983. External features in southern right whales (*Eubalaena australis*) and their use in identifying individuals. In *Communication and behavior of whales*. AAAS Selected Symposia Series, ed. R. Payne, 371–446. Boulder, CO: Westview Press.

Payne, K., P. Tyack, and R. Payne. 1983. Progressive changes in the songs of humpback whales (*Megaptera novaeangliae*): A detailed analysis of two seasons in Hawaii. In *Communication and behavior of whales. AAAS Selected Symposia Series*, ed. R. Payne, 9–57. Boulder, CO: Westview Press.

Perryman, W. L., and M. S. Lynn. 2002. Evaluation of nutritive condition and reproductive status of migrating gray whales (*Eschrichtius robustus*) based on analysis of photogrammetric data. *Journal of Cetacean Research Management* 4:155–164.

Rice, D. W. 1978. The humpback whale in the North Pacific: Distribution, exploitation and numbers. In Report on a workshop on problems related to humpback whales (*Megaptera novaeangliae*) in Hawaii, eds. K. S. Norris and R. R. Reeves, 29–44. Report MMC-77/03 to US Marine Mammal Commission, Washington D.C.

Rice, D. W., and A. A. Wolman. 1980. Census of humpback whales wintering around the Hawaiian Islands 1976–1979. Report to International Whaling Commission, Doc. No. Sc/31/38.

Ross, P. S., G. M. Ellis, M. G. Ikonomou, L. G. Barrett-Lennard, and R. F. Addison. 2000. High PCB concentrations in free-ranging Pacific killer whales, *Orcinus orca*: Effects of age, sex and dietary preference. *Marine Pollution Bulletin* 40: 504–515.

Rowntree, V., J. Darling, G. Silber, and M. Ferrari. 1980. Rare sighting of a right whale (*Eubalaena glacialis*) in Hawaii. *Canadian Journal of Zoology* 58:309–312.

Salden, D. R. 1990. Apparent feeding by a sub-adult humpback whale (*Megaptera novaeangliae*) off Maui, Hawaii. Report No. 4. Lahaina, HI: Hawaii Whale Research Foundation.

Salden, D. R. and J. Mickelson. 1999. Rare sighting of a North Pacific right whale (*Eubalaena glacialis*) in Hawaii. *Pacific Science* 53:341–345.

Salden, D. R., L. M. Herman, M. Yamaguchi, and F. Sato. 1999. Multiple visits of individual humpback whales (*Megaptera novaeangliae*) between the Hawaiian and Japanese winter grounds. *Canadian Journal of Zoology* 77:504–508.

Scammon, C. M. 1874. *The marine mammals of the northwestern coast of North America*. San Francisco, CA: John H. Carmany and Co.

Schofield, D. 2007. Pacific Islands Region marine mammal response network activity update, July 2007. Honolulu, HI: NOAA, Pacific Islands Regional Office.

———. 2008. Pacific Islands Region marine mammal response network activity update, January–April 2008. Honolulu, HI: NOAA, Pacific Islands Regional Office.

Silber, G. K. 1986. The relationship of social vocalizations to surface behavior and aggression in the Hawaiian humpback whale (*Megaptera novaeangliae*). *Canadian Journal of Zoology* 64:2075–2080.

Simao, S. M., and S. C. Moreira. 2005. Vocalizations of a female humpback whale in Arraial Do Cabo (R. J. Brazil). *Marine Mammal Science* 21:150–153.

Silvers, L. E., P. E. Rosel, and D. R. Salden. 2002. DNA sequence analysis of a North Pacific humpback whale (*Megaptera novaeangliae*) placenta. *Canadian Journal of Zoology* 80:1141–1144.

Silvers, L. E., and D. R. Salden. 1997. A large placenta encountered in the Hawaiian winter grounds of the humpback whale, *Megaptera novaeangliae*. *Marine Mammal Science* 13:711–716.

Smith, J. N., A. W. Goldizen, R. A. Dunlop, and M. J. Noad. 2008. Songs of male humpback whales, *Megaptera novaeangliae*, are involved in intersexual interactions. *Animal Behavior* 76:467–477.

Smultea, M. A. 1994. Segregation by humpback whale (*Megaptera novaeangliae*) cows with a calf in coastal habitat near the island of Hawaii. *Canadian Journal of Zoology* 72:805–811.

Spitz, S. S., L. M. Herman, and A. A. Pack. 2000. Measuring the sizes of humpback whales (*Megaptera novaeangliae*) through underwater videogrammetry. *Marine Mammal Science* 16:664–676.

Straley, J. M. 1999. Overwintering North Pacific humpback whales in Alaskan waters: Who are they? *Abstracts 13th Biennial Conference on the Biology of Marine Mammals*, Wailea, HI Nov. 28–Dec. 3, 1999.

Straley, J. M., C. M. Gabriele, C. S. Baker. 1994. Annual reproduction by individually identified humpback whales (*Megaptera novaeangliae*) in Alaskan waters. *Marine Mammal Science* 10:87–92.

Taber, S., and P. Thomas. 1984. Mother-infant interaction and behavioral development in southern right whales. *Behavior* 88:42–46.

Theodor, J. M. 2002. Artiodactyla. In *Encyclopedia of Marine Mammals*, ed. W. F. Perrin, B. Wursig, and J. G. M. Thewissen, 45–47. San Diego, CA: Academic Press.

Thompson, P. O., and W. A. Friedl. 1982. A long term study of low frequency sounds from several species of whales off Oahu, Hawaii. *Cetology* 45:1–19.

Tomilin, A. G. 1967. *Mammals of the U.S.S.R. and adjacent countries, Vol. 9. Cetacea* (trans. by O. Ronen from the 1957 Russian edition). Israel Program for Scientific Translations, Jerusalem.

Turvey, S. T., R. L. Pitman, B. L. Taylor, J. Barlow, T. Akamatsu, L. A. Barrett, X. Zhao, R. R. Reeves, B. S. Stewart, K. Wang, Z. Wei, X. Zhang, L. T. Pusser, M. Richlen, J. R. Brandon, and D. Wang. 2007. First human-caused extinction of a cetacean species. *Journal of the Royal Society, Biology Letters* 3:537–540.

Tyack, P. L. 1981. Interactions between singing Hawaiian humpback whales and conspecifics nearby. *Behavioral Ecology and Sociobiology* 8:105–116.

———. 1982. Humpback whales respond to sounds of their neighbors. PhD diss. Rockefeller Univ., New York.

———. 1983. Differential response of humpback whales, *Megaptera novaeangliae*, to playback of song or social sounds. *Behavioral Ecology and Sociobiology* 13:49–55.

Tyack, P., and H. Whitehead. 1983. Male competition in large groups of wintering humpback whales. *Behavior* 83:132–154.

Weller, D. W., B. Wursig, A. L. Bradford, A. M. Burdin, S. A. Blokhin, H. Minakuchi, and R. L. Brownell. 1999. Gray whales (*Eschrichtius robustus*) off Sakhalin Island, Russia: Seasonal and annual patterns of occurrence. *Marine Mammal Science* 15:1208–1227.

Wells, R. S., M. D. Scott, and A. B. Irvine. 1987. The social structure of free ranging bottlenose dolphins. In *Current Mammalogy Vol. 1*, ed. H. H. Genoways, 247–305. New York: Plenum Press.

Whitehead, H., and M. J. Moore. 1982. Distribution and movements of West Indian humpback whales in winter. *Canadian Journal of Zoology* 60:2203–2211.

Winn, H. E., and L. K. Winn. 1978. The song of the humpback whale, *Megaptera novaeangliae*, in the West Indies. *Marine Biology* 47:97–114.

Winn, H. E., W. L. Bischoff, and A. G. Turuski. 1973. Cytological sexing of cetacea. *Marine Biology* 23:343–346.

Winn, H. E., T. J. Thompson, W. C. Cummings, J. Hain, J. Hudnall, H. Hays, and W. W. Steiner. 1981. Song of the humpback whale — population comparisons. *Behavioral Ecology and Sociobiology* 8:41–46.

Wolman, A. A., and C. M. Jurasz. 1977. Humpback whales in Hawaii: Vessel census, 1976. *Marine Fisheries Review* 39:1–5.

Wrangham, R. W. 1986. Ecology and social relationships in two species of chimpanzees. In *Ecological aspects of social evolution in birds and mammals*, eds. D. I. Rubenstein and R. W. Wrangham, 354-378. Princeton, NJ: Princeton Univ. Press.

Wursig, B., and M. Wursig.1980. Behavior and ecology of the dusky dolphin, *Lagenorhynchus obscurus*, in the south Atlantic. *Fisheries Bulletin*. 77(4): 871–890.

Zoidis, A. M., M. A. Smultaea, A. S. Frankel, J. L. Hopkins, A. Day, A. S. McFarland, D. Fertl, and A. D. Whitt. 2008. Vocalizations produced by humpback whale (*Megaptera novaeangliae*) calves recorded in Hawaii. *Journal of the Acoustical Society of America* 123:1731–1746.

Website References

Convention on International Trade in Endangered Species of Wild Fauna and Flora (CITES). http://www.cites.org/

Government of Canada. Species at Risk Public Registry. http://www.sararegistry. gc.ca/approach/act/default_e.cfm

Greenpeace. http://www.greenpeace.org/international/

Hawaiian Islands Humpback Whale National Marine Sanctuary. http://hawaiihump-backwhale.noaa.gov/

International Whaling Commission. http://www.iwcoffice.org/

Japan Whaling Association. http://www.whaling.jp/english/index.html

National Resource Defense Council. http://www.nrdc.org/

NOAA Fisheries Office of Protected Resource: Protection. http://www.nmfs.noaa. gov/pr/

NOAA Fisheries Office of Protected Resources: Hawaii Guidelines. http://www.nmfs. noaa.gov/pr/education/hawaii

Sheep101. Info: lambing. http://www.sheep101.info/lambing.html

Whale Trust. http://www.whaletrust.org

Sources

*See **References** for the full citations.*

Chapter 1 **Whales!**
What Are They Doing Out There? (e.g. Clutton-Brock 1989, Emlen and Oring 1977, Krebs and Davies 1996), **The 1970s** (e.g. Bigg et al. 1976, Darling 1984, Glockner and Venus 1983, Herman 1979, Katona et al. 1979, Payne et al. 1983, Rice 1978, Wells et al. 1987), *I Was the Intruder* (Lindbergh 1967), *List of Cetaceans in Hawaii* (Barlow 2006, McSweeney et al. 2007, Rowntree et al. 1980, Salden and Mickelson 1999), **How Have We Learned About Humpback Whales?**, **Whaling Studies** (Chittleborough 1958, 1965, Dawbin 1966, Matthews 1937, Nishiwaki 1959, 1960, 1962, 1966), **Studying Living Whales at Sea** (e.g. Barlow 2006, Darling et al. 2006, Mate et al. 2007, Palsbol 1999), *Whalers in Hawaii* (Ellis 1991, Herman 1979), **What Are Researchers Doing Out There?** (e.g. Amos 1997, Darling and Bérubé 2001, Glockner 1983, Jaquet 2006, Katona et al. 1979, Payne et al. 1983, Perryman and Lynn 2002, Silber 1986, Spitz et al. 2000), *Humpback Whales* (Calambokidis et al. 2008, Chittleborough 1958, Clapham 1996, 2002, Dawbin 1966, Nishiwaki 1959).

Social Groups on the Breeding Grounds (Baker and Herman 1984, Clapham et al. 1992, Darling 1983, Darling and Bérubé 2001, Darling et al. 1983, Gabriele 1992, Glockner 1983, Glockner-Ferrari and Ferrari 1985, Mobley and Herman 1985, Winn et al. 1973).

Chapter 2 **'Hawaiian' Humpbacks**
Hawaii — A Migratory Destination, Why Migrate?, North Pacific Humpback Whale Migrations, *Where Are the 'Hawaiian' Humpbacks in Summer?* (Baker et al. 1986, Calambokidis et al. 2001, Chadwick 2007, Chittleborough 1958, Darling and Cerchio 1993, Darling and Jurasz 1983, Darling and McSweeney 1985, Dawbin 1966, Gabriele et al. 1996, Kellogg 1928, Mate et al. 2007, Salden et al. 1999, Scammon 1874), **'Missing' Whales?** (Brown et al. 1995, Craig and Herman 1997, Lockyer 1981, Straley 1999), **Breeding And Nursery Grounds, Geography or Behavior?** (Brown and Corkeron 1995, Clapham and Mattila 1990, Clark and Clapham 2004, Craig and Herman 1997, Glockner and Venus 1983, McSweeney et al. 1989, Noad and Cato 2007), **Where are the Whales in Hawaii?** (Cerchio et al. 1998, Craig and Herman 1997, Frankel et al. 1995, Glockner and Venus 1983, Mate et al. 1998, Mobley et al. 1994, 1999, Rice and Wolman 1980, Wolman and Jurasz 1977), **When Is The Best Time to See Whales?** (Au et al. 2000, Baker and Herman 1981, 1984, Chittleborough 1958, 1965, Craig and Herman 1997, Craig et al. 2003, Darling 1983, Dawbin 1966, Gabriele 1992, Glockner-Ferrari and Ferrari 1985, Herman and Antinoja 1977, Jones M. pers. comm. 2001, Mobley and Herman 1985, Mobley et al. 1999, Nishiwaki 1959, 1966, Thompson and Friedl 1982), **How Long Does Any Individual Whale Stay In Hawaii?** (Darling 1983, Darling and Morowitz 1986, Gabriele 1992, Glockner and Venus 1983, Glockner-Ferrari and Ferrari 1985, Mate et al. 2007, Mobley and Herman 1985), **Whale Movements Within The Hawaiian Islands** (Baker and Herman 1981, Cerchio et al. 1998, Craig and Herman 1997, Darling and Morowitz 1986, Mate et al. 1998, 2007, Mobley et al. 1999), **Is There Location-Specific Activity In The Islands?** (Baker and Herman 1981, Craig and Herman 2000, Frankel et al. 1995, Glockner-Ferrari and Ferrari 1985, Mobley and Herman 1985, Smultea 1994).

Chapter 3 **Breeding Season**
Seasonal Cycles of Humpback Whales (e.g. Chittleborough 1958, Clapham 1996, Dawbin 1966, Lockyer 1984, Matthews 1937, Nishiwaki 1966), **How Have We Learned About Humpback Reproductive Cycles?** (Baker and Herman 1984, Baker et al. 1987, Chittleborough 1965, Clapham 1992, Clapham and Mayo 1987, 1990, Darling 1983, Dawbin 1966, Gabriele 1992, Glockner-Ferrari and Ferrari 1985, Matthews 1937, Nishiwaki 1959, 1960, 1962, 1966, Straley et al. 1994, Tomlin 1967, Tyack and Whitehead 1983), **Sexual Maturity And Birth Rate** (Baker et al. 1987, Barlow and Clapham 1996, Chittleborough 1958, 1965, Clapham and Mayo 1987, Clapham and Mayo 1990, Darling 1983, Gabriele 1992, Gabriele et al. 2007, Glockner and Venus 1983, Glockner-Ferrari and Ferrari 1984, 1985, 1990, Matthews 1937, Mobley and Herman 1985, Nishiwaki 1959, Straley et al. 1994), **When Mating Behavior and Pregnancies Don't Add Up** (Chittleborough 1958, Gabriele 1992, Glockner-Ferrari and Ferrari 1985, Mikhalev 2000 (in Noad and Cato 2007), Mobley and Herman 1985, Straley et al. 1994), **Mating Time, Estrus: Occurrence, Recurrence, and Duration** (Chittleborough 1958, 1965, Darling 1983, Dawbin 1966, Gabriele 1992, Glockner-Ferrari and Ferrari 1990, Matthews 1937, Mikhalev 2000 (in Noad and Cato 2007), Mobley and Herman 1985, Nishiwaki 1959, 1960, 1962, Tomlin 1967), *Estrus Cycles and Duration* (Sheep 101. Info (website), Theodor 2002), **Male Behavior Indicates Female Estrus** (Au et al. 2000, Baker and Herman 1984, Cartwright 1999, Darling 1983, Gabriele 1992, Glockner-Ferrari and Ferrari 1990, Mobley and Herman 1985), *How Do Male Whales Know a Female Is Ready to Mate?* (e.g. Krebs and Davies 1996, Mead and Gold 2002), **What We See And Why** (Baker and Herman 1984, Cartwright 1999, Craig et al. 2003, Darling 1983, Darling et al. 1983, Gabriele 1992, Glockner and Venus 1983, Glockner-Ferrari and Ferrari 1985, Mobley and Herman 1985, Tyack and Whitehead 1983).

Chapter 4 **Mating — The Male Perspective**
Singing, Escorting, Competing, And (Perhaps) Cooperating (Au et al. 2000, Baker and Herman 1984, Brown and Corkeron 1995, Clapham et al. 1992, Darling 1983, Darling et al. 1983, Darling and Bérubé 2001, Darling et al. 2006, Frankel et al. 1995, Gabriele 1992, Glockner-Ferrari and Ferrari 1985, Mobley and Herman 1985, Tyack 1981, 1983, Tyack and Whitehead 1983), **Male/Male Behavior, Singing** (Au et al. 2000, Clark and Clapham 2004, Darling 1983, Darling and Bérubé 2001, Darling et al. 1983, 2006, Glockner 1983, Glockner-Ferrari and Ferrari 1985, Mattila et al. 1987, McSweeney et al. 1989, Payne and McVay 1971, Payne et al. 1983, Smith et al. 2008, Winn and Winn 1978, Winn et al. 1973), *Bermuda and Whale Song* (Bermuda Zoological Society 1983, Dietz 1982), *The Song* (Cerchio et al. 2001, Noad et al. 2000, Payne and Guinee 1983, Payne and McVay 1971, Payne and Payne 1985, Payne et al. 1983, Winn et al. 1981), **Why Do They Sing?** (Au et al. 2000, Baker and Herman 1984, Brown and Corkeron 1995, Cerchio et al. 2001, Chu 1988, Chu and Harcourt 1986, Clapham 1996, Clapham and Mattila 1990, Clark and Clapham 2004, Darling 1983, Darling and Bérubé 2001, Darling et al. 2006, Frankel et al. 1995, Frazer and Mercado 2000, Helweg et al. 1992, Helweg and Herman 1994, Mobley and Herman 1985, Mobley et al. 1988, Noad et al. 2000, Payne et al. 1983, Silber 1986, Smith et al. 2008, Tyack 1981, 1983, Tyack and Whitehead 1983, Winn and Winn 1978), **Males Joining Singers** (Darling 1983, Darling and Bérubé 2001, Darling et al. 2006, Frankel et al. 1995, Helweg et al. 1992, Mobley et al. 1988, Smith et al. 2008, Tyack 1981, 1983), **Males Around Females, Accompanying a Female, What, Then, Is the Role of the Escort?** (Baker and Herman 1984, Chittleborough 1953, Clapham et al. 1992, Darling 1983, Darling et al. 1983, Frankel et al. 1995, Gabriele 1992, Glockner 1983, Glockner and Venus 1983, Glockner-Ferrari and Ferrari 1985, Herman and Antinoja 1977, Herman and Tavolga 1980, Mobley and Herman 1985, Tyack 1981, Tyack and Whitehead 1983), **Competition for Access to Females, *Threats and Full-On Brawls*** (Darling et al. 2006, Frankel et al. 1995, Glockner-Ferrari and Ferrari 1985, Mobley and Herman 1985, Mobley et al. 1988, Pack et al. 1998, Silber 1986, Tyack 1981, 1982, 1983, Tyack and Whitehead 1983), **Social Sounds** (Silber 1986, Tyack and Whitehead 1983), **Cooperation for Access to a Female** (Brown and Corkeron 1995, Clapham et al. 1992, Darling and Bérubé 2001, Darling et al. 2006, Frankel et al. 1995, Pack et al. 1998, Tyack and Whitehead 1983), Males Caring for

Other Males? (Pack et al. 1998).

Chapter 5 **Mating — The Female Perspective**
Pairing With, Avoiding and (Perhaps) Choosing Males (Baker 1985, Baker and Herman 1984, Clapham et al. 1992, Craig et al. 2002, Darling 1983, Emlen and Oring 1977, Gabriele 1992, Glockner 1983, Glockner-Ferrari and Ferrari 1985, Herman and Antinoja 1977, Mobley et al. 1988, Tyack 1981, Tyack and Whitehead 1983), **Female Roles** (Chittleborough 1965, Craig et al. 2002, Darling 1983, Dawbin 1966, Gabriele 1992, Glockner 1983, Glockner and Venus 1983, Glockner-Ferrari and Ferrari 1985, 1990), **What We See, Female with an Adult Male, Female with Multiple Males, Female Discouraging Males** (Baker and Herman 1984, Brown and Corkeron 1995, Clapham et al. 1992, Craig and Herman 1997, Craig et al. 2002, Darling 1983, Darling and Bérubé 2001, Darling et al. 1983, 2006, Gabriele 1992, Glockner-Ferrari and Ferrari 1985, Mattila et al. 1989, Mobley and Herman 1985, Mobley et al. 1988, Silber 1986, Tyack 1981, Tyack and Whitehead 1983), **What We Don't (or Rarely) See, Females Are Rarely Alone, Females Do Not Associate with Other Females, Females Do Not Join Singers,** *Copulation?* (Baker 1985, Baker and Herman 1984, Cartwright R. pers comm. 2001, Clapham et al. 1992, Darling 1983, Gabriele 1992, Glockner 1983, Glockner-Ferrari and Ferrari 1985, Herman and Antinoja 1977, Mobley et al. 1988, Pack et al. 2002, Smith et al. 2008, Tyack 1981, Tyack and Whitehead 1983), **Mating Situations,** *Rewinding History: When Does Mating Occur?* (Darling 1983), **Female/Male Pair, Females Leading Multiple Males** (Baker and Herman 1984, Chittleborough 1965, Clapham et al. 1992, Darling 1983, Darling and Bérubé 2001, Darling et al. 1983, 2006, Gabriele 1992, Glockner-Ferrari and Ferrari 1985, Mattila et al. 1989, Mobley and Herman 1985, Mobley et al. 1988, Silber 1986, Tyack 1981, Tyack and Whitehead 1983), **Do Females Choose Their Mates Based On Their Song?** (Chu 1988, Chu and Harcourt 1986, Clapham 1996, Clark and Clapham 2004, Darling and Bérubé 2001, Darling et al. 2006, Frankel et al. 1995, Gabriele C. pers. comm. 2001, Helweg et al. 1992, Mobley and Herman 1985, Medrano et al. 1994, Mobley et al. 1988, Smith et al. 2008, Tyack 1981, Tyack and Whitehead 1983, Winn and Winn 1978).

Chapter 6 **Newborns and Juveniles**
Maternal Priorities, Those Persistent Males, Avoiding the Neighbors, Predators (Chittleborough 1953, Darling 1990, Glockner and Venus 1983, Glockner-Ferrari and Ferrari 1985, 1990, Jones and Swartz 1984, Jones M. pers comm. 2001, Nicklin F. pers. comm. 2000, Smultea 1994, Taber and Thomas 1984, Whitehead and Moore 1982, Wursig and Wursig 1980), **A Birth — Who Will See it First?** (Cartwright 2005, Chittleborough 1958, Darling 1983, Glockner-Ferrari and Ferrari 1985, Nishiwaki 1959, Silvers et al. 2002, Silvers and Salden 1997), **When Do We See Humpback Calves?** (Baker and Herman 1984, Craig and Herman 1997, Darling 1983, Gabriele 1992, Glockner 1983, Glockner and Venus 1983, Glockner-Ferrari and Ferrari 1985), **Newborns — How Do They Spend Their First Weeks In Hawaii?, Travel — The Most Common Activity!, Resting, Nursing, Play** (Cartwright 1999, 2005, Clapham 1996, Craig and Herman 1997, Darling 1983, Gabriele 1992, Glockner and Venus 1983, Glockner-Ferrari and Ferrari 1985, Mate et al. 1998, Mobley and Herman 1985), **Mother/Calf Communication** (Glockner-Ferrari and Ferrari 1985, Nicklin F. pers. comm. 2000, Simao and Moreira 2005, Zoidis et al. 2008), **The Calf And The Escort(s), Escorts: Are They Hired Guns?** (Cartwright 1999, Darling et al. 1983, 2006, Glockner-Ferrari and Ferrari 1985, Mesnick 1997, Mobley and Herman 1985, Wrangham 1986), **Juveniles** (Craig and Herman 1997, Darling 1983, Darling and Bérubé 2001, Dawbin 1966, Gabriele 1992, Glockner-Ferrari and Ferrari 1985, Salden 1989).

Chapter 7 **Whales and Us**
The 1900s, Whaling, Recovery, The Numbers (Baker and Herman 1987, Calambokidis et
al. 1997, 2008, Cerchio 1998, Darling et al. 1983, Darling and Morowitz 1986, Doroshenko 2000,
Herman and Antinoja 1977, Rice 1978, Rice and Wolman 1980), *Not All Whale Populations Are
Recovering* (Best et al. 2001, Clapham et al. 1999, De Guise et al. 1995, Ross et al. 2000, Rowntree et
al. 1980, Salden and Mickelson 1999, Turvey et al. 2007, Weller et al. 1999), **Hawaiian Humpbacks
Today, The Promise — Science and Education, Protection, Science, Education,
Whale Watching** (Convention on International Trade in Endangered Species of Wild Fauna and Flora
(CITES) (website), Hoyt 2001, International Whaling Commission (website), NOAA Office of Protected
Resources (website)), *The Hawaiian Islands Humpback Whale National Marine Sanctuary*
(The Hawaiian Islands Humpback Whale National Marine Sanctuary (website)), *Approaching Whales
in Hawaii* (NOAA Office of Protected Resources Marine Mammal Guidelines Hawaii (website)), **The
Threats, Threats to Individuals: Entanglements and Collisions, Entanglements,
Vessel–Whale Collisions** (Lyman and Matilla 2007, 2008, Schofield 2007, 2008), **Threats to
Populations: Hunting, Food, and Habitat, Commercial Whaling, Competition
with Human Fisheries, Changing Natural Habitats: Pollution to Climate Change,
Cumulative Impacts — Adding Them All Together** (Clapham et al. 1999, Darling 1990,
Greenpeace International (website), The International Whaling Commission (website), Japan Whaling
Association (website)), *The Down-Listing and Whaling Debate* (San Jose Mercury News, June
8, 2007), *Extreme Noise Pollution: Naval Active Sonar Systems* (Miller et al. 2000, the
National Resources Defense Council (website)), *Climate Change* (e.g. Committee on Abrupt Climate
Change and National Research Council 2002, Elliott and Simmonds 2007).

Appendix **Agreements and Laws Protecting Humpback Whales**
(The International Whaling Commission (website), NOAA Office of Protected Resources (website), and
the Government of Canada Species At Risk Public Registry (website)).

Actions and Postures
(Darling 1983, Gabriele 1992 (adapted from Bauer 1986 and Helweg 1989), Glockner-Ferrari and Ferrari
1985).

Index

*Numbers in **bold** are illustrations and tables.*

Biographies

Jim Darling

Jim began studying whales in the 1970s, developing individual photo-identification techniques for gray whales off Vancouver Island. His first experience with Hawaii's whales was during winter surfing trips, and this eventually led him to a PhD at the University of California Santa Cruz, researching humpback whale abundance and behavior. Since then, Jim has studied whales throughout the North Pacific and worldwide, but he returns to Maui annually to his focus on humpback singers and songs. Jim first met Flip Nicklin (an expert free diver) in Maui in 1979 and asked him to photograph singers without disturbing them.

Flip Nicklin

Flip's introduction to Maui's whales in the late 1970s inspired him to embark on a brilliant career in underwater photography. Since then, Flip has produced 20 *National Geographic* stories on whales and dolphins. He has set the bar not only for whale photography but also for photo-documentation assisting whale research. In winter, Flip can usually be found in his West Maui cottage, waiting for calm waters and, with Darling, still trying to understand what singers are doing out there. One wall of his cottage is adorned with three striking paintings that can be the work of only one artist — Sue Barnes.

FRAN GEALER

Susan Wallace Barnes

Sue grew up surfing in California and Hawaii in the late 1950s and early 60s, and she has never broken that tie with the ocean. Simply, Susan Wallace Barnes's art takes us to the beach and reminds us of its value. From her home above Carmel Bay (and one of the most beautiful beaches in the world), with whales often passing along its shores, she has spent a lifetime increasing public awareness and appreciation for the ocean. When asked to provide illustrations for this book, the answer was 'yes' in a millisecond, with the lament that she was not doing enough. . . .

ED LANE

WHALE TRUST

Making the world a better place.

RESEARCH • EDUCATION • CONSERVATION

www.whaletrust.org

Fresh Courage Take

Fresh Courage Take
New Directions by Mormon Women

Jamie Zvirzdin, editor

with a foreword by
Joanna Brooks

Signature Books | 2015 | Salt Lake City

Design by Jason Francis

20   19   18   17   16   15   6   5   4   3   2   1

LIBRARY OF CONGRESS CATALOGING-IN-PUBLICATION DATA

Fresh courage take : new directions by Mormon women /
Jamie Zvirzdin, editor; with a foreword by Joanna Brooks.
    pages cm
    ISBN 978-1-56085-240-7
1. Mormon women. I. Zvirzdin, Jamie, 1983–, editor.
    BX8643.W66F74 2015
    289.3'32082—dc23
                            2015019399

Contents

Foreword

Joanna Brooks

It's time to dive into these pages and find in the company of these women a delicious freedom, "freedom from feeling beholden to an unrealistic cultural standard," as Jamie Zvirzdin writes. "The freedom to stop mimicking who we think we *ought* to be and start thinking about who we *want* to be."

Given the significance of gender in Latter-day Saint theology, Mormon women have always lived with an unusual caliber of expectations. The right to set aside unrealistic expectations and to find one's own unique and divinely appointed purpose is one of the great gifts Mormon women can give each other. And it's the gift the essays in *Fresh Courage Take* freely give.

These are honest Mormon feminist voices—the voices of those who practice a feminism that is about "cooperation and compassion," as Marcee Monroe writes, a feminism that values plain-spoken solidarity over the quiet perfectionist competition that too often infuses Mormon women's relationships. Many of the women in this volume are accomplished and talented writers, yet some of them are writing for the first time about their faith. Their voices are a welcome contribution to the diversity and breadth of Mormon literature.

Our faith has taught us that this life is about learning our way toward joy, and the example of Eve has demonstrated to us that growth means working hard and taking risks. The women in this wonderful collection accept hard work and real soul-searching as the price of knowledge and freedom. As contributor Erika Ball writes, "It is liberating to let myself be both a woman of faith and a woman of intelligence. I give you the same permission, if you need it: don't let someone else define your faith or your intelligence or tell you your faith is somehow different and distinct from your intelligence."

This book will give you permission to stop accepting other people's definitions of a womanly ideal. Permission to stop saving for cosmetic surgery. Permission to leave the dust bunnies alone. To love your brain. To honor your body. To accept gifts from strangers. Maybe even to wear pants to church, if you'd like.

Take courage, sister. Your time has come.

Acknowledgments

In his poem "Ulysses," Alfred Lord Tennyson wrote, "I am a part of all that I have met," something I feel resoundingly about the women who participated in this project, since they have so positively influenced the person I am today. Working on this book together has been a wonderful and heart-expanding collaboration. My sincere thanks, ladies.

Additionally, Daryle Newman, my brilliant Australian muse, has been a constant source of encouragement from the beginning. Camille Strate Fairbanks and Suzy Bills spent a great deal of time and energy reviewing the essays. Sven Birkerts gave thoughtful input on my essays as I wrestled with them, and Colleen Whitley delivered the physical manuscript to Signature, as I was in the Marshall Islands at the time. John Hatch and Ron Priddis at Signature have been our patient and supportive editors, and it was a pleasure to watch Jason Francis design this book. Thanks also goes to the other staff at Signature for their help in bringing this project to fruition.

My parents and siblings have loved me without ceasing, most importantly during critical junctures when I chose new directions for myself. Most of all, I thank my husband for his encouragement and for our many discussions over the years about what a truly equal partnership means to us.

I would also like to acknowledge the women in the world who endure abuse, criticism, loneliness, and despair, not just in faraway places but among us, wherever we are: women who suffer because they cannot see their way forward. I hope that if this book falls into their hands, it will help them formulate a plan for recovery and peace.

Introduction

For two years, beginning in 2011, I lived on a sliver of sand in the middle of the Pacific Ocean—one of those places on the map that is always squished to one edge or the other, unworthy of center stage to a Eurocentric, north-is-up, Mercator-projected world. I lived on the lagoon side of Majuro Atoll in the Marshall Islands, and from my back porch, which hung over the bright blue-and-green water, I could see the enormous lagoon stretching from my left peripheral view clear to my right. A volcano used to live and spit there, but over the span of seventy million years, it slowly sank into the deep and left a built-up crescent of coral about thirty miles long and only a few hundred yards wide at most. The atoll supported hardy vegetation, some critters, and eventually, some brave, seafaring Marshallese ancestors. Fast-forward four thousand years, and there I was, living on the edge of an old volcano crater in the North Pacific.

It's a pretty wild experience to kayak across the lagoon by yourself to some isolated coral islands on the other side of the atoll. There, the ebb and flow of the tide between islands reminds you of the movement of sharks—and then you realize that the movements *are* sharks, sharks that feed on the fish coming in and out with the tide. Paddling over to these islands, I often caught myself looking down into the water, gulping at the depth, and resolutely looking away to avoid dizziness. The lagoon is 200 feet deep, which is nothing next to the 7,000-foot drop-off just outside the atoll. The depth is stunning, and the thought of snorkeling in those terror-filled waters frightened me.

While my husband worked at the US Embassy on Majuro, I edited science articles and took care of our son, who had just turned one. To say we were isolated would be an understatement. We were 2,400 miles from Cairns, Australia; 2,300 miles from Honolulu; and 3,600 miles from Shanghai, China.[1] The potable water on the island is largely dependent on the rain, the electricity (if you're rich enough to have it) goes out regularly, leprosy and tuberculosis are recurring problems, falling coconuts *do* present a real danger, and any infrastructure on the atoll, financed by well-meaning foreign countries, rusts to red and brown bits before your eyes in the salty air. While the State Department would have stepped in to help us if there had been an accident, I prayed frequently that nothing would happen, especially to my son, since

---

1. For the sake of comparison, Los Angeles is 2,400 miles from New York, and it is another 2,500 miles from California to Hawaii.

the only hospital was infested with rats and cockroaches. During especially high tides, the waves washed over our footpaths and roads, and typhoon-like storms made us feel that the gods—at least the tropical ones—were upset. I can remember a large, angry wave hitting my bedroom window in the thick of night: the next morning I saw where the window's seal had splintered along the edges of the frame. As the water chipped away at our land-borne confidence, life felt very fragile.

Yet I had never felt so free and consistently at peace. Living on Majuro was the catalyst I needed for some serious introspection. It was my tropical Walden, although my "pond" happened to be over a hundred square miles of lagoon and connected to nearly 800,000 square miles of ocean. The incessant background noise of urban life with its fiber-optic Internet connections and entertainment opportunities had vanished, aided by the fact that we did not own a TV. Marshallese culture, vastly different from American norms (including matrilineal land inheritances), shocked me out of my own worldview. I began thinking in that calm, slow place about the cultural habits I had presumed were universal, including the details of human relationships, gender identity, and what constituted a productive, satisfying life. (The idea that productivity was a crucial ingredient for a satisfying life was itself called into question.) I had thought that what was normal and fulfilling for one woman in one part of the world would be more or less the same every-where. A woman should think this way, behave that way, marry a husband and rear her children just so. Yet many of these maxims I had accumulated didn't seem to apply at the remote outposts of human existence. The tenuous environment and constant struggle for resources have dictated the etiquette and morality of Pacific Islanders for thousands of years. What was right to me was more often an American or a Utahan concept rather than a universal one.

In April 2012, while I was struggling with my chang-ing worldview, I started to contact women to contribute to this book—all of them acquaintances of mine from various stages in my life and all members of the Church of Jesus Christ of Latter-day Saints (LDS). I remember the sweltering, sunny day I first emailed Colleen Whit-ley, my freshman English teacher at Brigham Young University, about the project. Borrowing the neighbor's Wi-Fi connection since ours was down, I sat in my bro-ken white plastic chair under the neighbor's coconut tree, which had been trimmed back to avoid hazards, and almost immediately I received an enthusiastic response back from Colleen.

Sitting at the edge of a lagoon-covered volcano while hermit crabs climbed onto my bare feet, I was able to contact all the women who ultimately contributed to this collection. I had known Karen Challis Critchfield since middle school; others I met at BYU or in LDS church congregations ("wards"); some of the women were friends of friends I had connected with online. My life has been enriched by all of them, and I was pleased that they responded so positively. I asked if they would share their perspectives on being a Mormon woman by choosing their own specific topics and styles of presentation. Each in her own way challenges the idea that there is one right way to be a woman. I found their collective breadth of experiences eye-opening and humbling.

As a quick summary, Colleen Whitley is a retired professor with grandchildren who recalls her involvement as a test case for women's rights at BYU in 1967. Erika Ball has worked as a statistician in Washington, DC, where she learned to trust her intellect; she encourages other women to do so as well. Rachael Decker Bailey made a difficult migration from academia to motherhood, while Karen Challis Critchfield found passion again after feeling that something was missing in her life as a stay-at-home mother. Marcee Monroe learned to type one-handed with a newborn on her lap and became successful both as a devoted mother and as a champion for feminism.

Breaking stereotypes, Carli Anderson, Brooke Stoneman, and Sylvia Lankford write from outside the traditional Mormon family, Carli finding contentment and purpose as a single-adult woman, Brooke coming to terms with infertility and wrestling with the implications of unanswered prayers, and Sylvia relating her conversion to the LDS Church and social challenges as a black woman (in a white congregation) who divorced and had to adjust as a single parent in a family-oriented church.

Others tackle controversial issues such as the patriarchal church structure and reclaiming the power of one's own body (Rachel Brown), attitudes toward homosexuals (Ashley Mae Hoiland), and the promotion of the idealized woman (Jamie Zvirzdin). Finally, Camille Strate Fairbanks, the twelfth member of our homespun quorum, had a less-than-ecstatic experience with pregnancy and explores what we mean when we talk about the divine nature of women. A more complete description of these wonderful friends can be found at the end of this book. For now, I will simply say by way of introduction that I have been fortunate to know them.

Obviously, this compilation represents only a fraction of the diverse experiences of Mormon women everywhere. Ours is a pluralistic feminism—or, as Robin Morgan, cofounder of the Woman's Media Center nonprofit group, has written, "I call it feminisms—plural."[2] What is most important is that we choose to act for ourselves instead of being acted upon; we believe that letting others chart our path for us can lead to undesired

2. Qtd. in Jenna Goudreau, "Who's Afraid of Post-Feminism? What It Means to Be a Feminist Today," *Forbes*, Dec. 13, 2011.

destinations. Choosing to marry, have many children, and stay at home full-time with those children is a legitimate and honorable life path, but we also acknowledge this path as only one of *many* legitimate and honorable paths. All paths, traditional or not, turn and twist, fork, double back on themselves, take us to the grand heights of human joy and to the deep valleys of acute suffering. Life is hardly ever a straight and narrow road.

It is important to note that the contributors to this book do not speak for the LDS Church. We speak for ourselves. Even so, because the essays range in tone from orthodox to heterodox, readers will probably agree with some of the content and reject other parts of it. The important thing is to consider it—and see the humanity of the woman behind the choice we may personally oppose.

It can be tempting to vilify women who take a different cultural path than we might. Such disparagement brings to mind the French phrase *panier de crabes* (basket of crabs), a phrase used to describe a fierce rivalry among individuals or groups. On Majuro, I was accustomed to seeing hundreds of skittering white, pink, red, and brown crabs on the shoreline; when we'd approach their holes, the larger ones would stand up and put their claws in the air, ready for a fight. At a Marshallese grocery store one day, I saw a cardboard box full of massive, brown-black crabs, whose cold fury gave me the shivers. Crabs do indeed struggle to escape their prison but pull the most advanced crab down when it gets to the top. Mary Elizabeth Williams wrote about the "Mom War" where this crab-in-a-bucket mentality is only too apparent:

> My dual identity [as an employed mother who works from home] has over the years enabled me to be a spy in two houses. I have sat in friends' living rooms on long, lazy play dates, listening to mothers complain about those terrible working moms [and] … say crappy things about how they just cannot understand how any woman could leave her precious baby, who brag that what they do, in comparison, is the very best and most important job in the whole wide world. I have witnessed the grudging tolerance for those who "have to" work, contrasted with the copious disdain still reserved for those careerist freaks. …
>
> But I have also heard working moms congratulate themselves for being "real" feminists, and ponder when those sorry hausfraus are ever going to "get a life." I was recently at an event where a fellow working mother cast a long, cold look over at a flock of stay-at-home mothers huddled together, and sniffed, "I have nothing to say to those people." And it breaks my heart to see this stuff, at a flash point in our history when our value in the workplace and our reproductive freedoms are under such vicious assault on so many fronts.[3]

---

3. Mary Elizabeth Williams, "End the Mom War," *Salon*, Apr. 13, 2012.

Although Williams was speaking specifically about stay-at-home mothers and working mothers, the same harsh judgment is found the world over between single and married females, straight and LGBTQ women, Mormon and ex-Mormon women, educated and uneducated women, breastfeeding and bottle-feeding women, those who support women's ordination and those who don't, women who choose to have children and those who don't, and women of different races. Any line we can draw in the sand, we do. As I continue to meet all sorts of women around the world, I can now see that trying to put a given individual into a particular category has the potential of being coercive and divisive, even when done with the best of intent. Humanity is divided into spectra, not into pink and blue boxes with preset expectations.

Unfortunately, throughout the world psychological and spiritual bullying seem to be alive and well, where shame, fear, and passive-aggressive behavior are strategies people employ to enforce homogeneity. This is evident in church circles as well as elsewhere. You would think it would be difficult to look at the depth of human differences and not acknowledge the diversity of life. Yet many resolutely choose to look away. Well-meaning people, even without intending to, can create an enormous amount of pressure on others by assuming that one path—the path they happen to be on, usually—will undoubtedly bring the same measure of happiness to everyone else. It is like someone who insists that there is only one right answer to a multi-variable equation.

Mormon women also need to know that their priesthood leaders are not the final arbiters of their lives, nor are priesthood leaders incapable of error. We have been taught, as a fundamental principle of our religion, that each of us has personal agency, meaning the power to think for ourselves and to say no when necessary, even to a leader who says he is speaking for God. As well-intentioned as most leaders are, women cannot capitulate this basic responsibility, nor should a leader put himself into the position of overriding a member's volition. In fact, if this principle is violated, it should be reported to higher authorities or even to the police.

The story of Eve, whether one believes in a literal Eve and Adam or not, is the story of a new direction. Eve chose to eat the forbidden fruit without permission from either God or her husband. In the LDS understanding of this story, Eve made the right decision for the benefit of all human progress and happiness, as well as for her own chance to learn and experience joy in this life.

While the forbidden fruit is often depicted as an apple (possibly because of a Latin pun on *mālum*, apple, and *mălum*, evil), some Jewish scholars hold that the Tree of Knowledge was a pomegranate tree. The pomegranate, which symbolized fruitfulness for them, appeared on the robes of Jewish priests. However, the pomegranate has had many other poignant associations through time and culture: a symbol of royalty for the ancient Greeks; a symbol of ambition and prosperity for the ancient Egyptians; a symbol of the suffering and resurrection of Jesus Christ for early Christians, as well as the idea that each individual seed belonged to a communal whole. As the symbolism of the pomegranate varies, so do each woman's needs, desires, and joys. Each woman should feel free to choose the interpretation that best suits her life while still feeling that she belongs to the great sisterhood of humanity.

It was several weeks before I found the courage to put on snorkeling gear and walk into the lagoon. Occasionally a purple-and-white-checkered baby diaper had floated past our house, and we had seen dead dolphins, cats, and pigs drift by. But the blue water continued to beckon, and I came to appreciate the lagoon on an entirely different dimension, in a direction perpendicular to my original kayaking route.

At first I clung to my husband, making it hard for either of us to swim as I worried about the jellyfish, sharks, the strong current, and the *E. coli* in the water. While there were plenty of beer bottles and tires and white plastic bags snagged on sickly-looking coral, this underwater world proved to be ablaze with yellow-and-black angelfish; orange-and-white clownfish that are all male until the dominant one in the group turns female; light purple, white, and orange coral, complex and delicate;

neon turquoise fish; purple-and-green parrotfish; and my favorite, the multicolored, otherworldly Picasso triggerfish. I eventually snorkeled by myself.

It takes a soft heart—the Marshallese would say a soft throat—to consider perspectives that differ from our own. Reading about the experiences of others allows us to live a piece of their lives and yet remain ourselves—our wiser selves, with any luck. Tension is a constant of human existence and will always be felt among people who are different from each other. In LDS culture, *tension* is often confused with *contention*, and because the devil is said to be the founder of contention, uncomfortable feelings are filed away on a shelf. But shelves become heavy, collapse, and cause damage if not properly taken care of. Mormons have a long tradition of being truth seekers, but what we do with the truths we find is a measure of our maturity and character.

So we invite you to pull up a chair, dismantle your shelves, and break open a pomegranate with us. Here are our truths, may they set us free.

1 | Changing Tides for Mormon Women

Colleen Whitley

When the LDS Church was organized in 1830, American women had few rights—they couldn't vote, inherit property in their own names, or have custody of children in cases of divorce. Additionally, corporal punishment by husbands (read: spousal abuse) was not uncommon and was occasionally upheld by law.[1] Ironically, the growth of women's clubs would change not only the status of women but the status of all Americans. The female dependents of wealthy men in the nineteenth century were expected to engage in "good works" and self-improvement, and so they organized book clubs, gardening clubs—all kinds of clubs—and the discussions and actions among their members led to some of the greatest social and political changes of the next century: abolition of slavery, voting rights for

---

1. For example, in *State v. Rhodes* and *State v. Oliver* in North Carolina, the courts found that husbands who had beaten their wives with switches no bigger than the size of their thumbs were not guilty of assault. See also Ken Burns and Paul Barnes, *Not for Ourselves Alone: The Story of Elizabeth Cady Stanton and Susan B. Anthony* (New York: Knopf, 1999).

women, even things as mundane and essential as the installation of city sewers.[2]

Within the LDS Church, however, the position of women was vastly different. On April 6, 1830, when the church was born in New York with about sixty people present, the founders included women. However, to meet the legal requirements of the state of New York, only six people needed to be listed on the corporate documents, and the six were men, concealing the liberal social makeup of the church from its beginning. The prophet Joseph Smith said of the women's auxiliary twelve years later that "the Church was never fully organized until" the Relief Society was founded and "the women were thus organized."[3]

By the time the Saints had migrated two thousand miles west from the place of the church's origin, the idea of excluding women from jobs, votes, or education appears to have all but disappeared. Brigham Young, president after Joseph Smith, encouraged women to be writers, teachers, doctors. Polygamy, or plural marriage, actually allowed women far more options than did traditional nineteenth-century marriages.[4] For example, it

---

2. Karen J. Blair, *The Clubwoman as Feminist: True Womanhood Redefined, 1868–1914* (New York: Holmes & Meier, 1980).

3. "Story of the Organization of the Relief Society," *Relief Society Magazine*, Mar. 1919, 129.

4. In most plural marriages, "wife" did not carry its usual meanings or responsibilities. See the articles by eight contributors in

greatly aided women who needed to travel to the East Coast to study in fields like medicine, and their "sister wives" cared for their children and helped foot the bills for school. In fact, one of the things East Coast men feared most about polygamy was the freedom it gave women, although in fact only a few women took advantage of the opportunities polygamy offered.[5]

Women in early Utah had the same access to education and civil rights as men. In 1850 the University of Deseret (now the University of Utah) opened as a co-ed institution long before this was common elsewhere, while women in other areas of the nation and world would battle for years to be allowed equal access to education. In the church, women had always voted to sustain leaders and officers, so it is probably not surprising that both women and men voted in the first territorial elections in 1850 and continued to vote until Congress took that and other rights away from them. Under the guise of protecting women, anti-polygamy legislation, from the Morrill Anti-Polygamy Act in 1862 to the Edmunds-Tucker Act in 1887, banned women from voting, forced them to testify in court against their husbands, took away the right of children from polygamous marriages to inherit property,

---

Colleen Whitley, ed., *Brigham Young's Homes* (Logan: Utah State University Press, 2002). Appendix B lists all of Brigham Young's wives and includes their prior and subsequent marriages and children.

5. Jesse Embry, "The History of Polygamy," *History to Go*, Utah State Historical Society website, historytogo.utah.gov.

and denied women the right to inherit property in their own names. Granting such rights was anathema to the non-Mormon male establishment. Ironically (or perhaps appropriately), the right of women to inherit property in their own names was first restored in Utah and later granted to women in the rest of the country in the early twentieth century. This came about through a case involving Susanna Bransford, Utah's so-called Silver Queen, who sued to be able to inherit her husband's shares in the Silver King Mine. She won, in part, because the mine's business partners testified in her favor. It was "one of the most important cases from a legal standpoint that has ever come before any court in the West," one observer noted.[6]

Eventually, individual states and territories passed laws giving women the vote in local elections even though they were still denied the right to vote in presidential elections. On December 10, 1869, Wyoming granted women local suffrage; Utah did so the next day, and Colorado followed soon after. The first subsequent election was in Utah, with women arriving at the polls in Wyoming and Colorado soon thereafter. Utah women did not just vote, they ran for office. In 1898, Martha Hughes Cannon became the first woman in the nation elected to a state senate; she served with Harriet Merrill

6. "Legal Record," *Argus*, Dec. 29, 1894; for the full story, see Judy Dykman and Colleen Whitley, *The Silver Queen* (Logan: Utah State University Press, 1998), 37–43.

Horne, the first woman elected to a state-level house of representatives.[7] And in 1912, the little Mormon town of Kanab on the Arizona border became the first city in the nation to have an all-female town council.[8]

To this point in history, most families lived on farms and ranches and engaged in occupations that required full-time attention by all the adults in the family, as well as the children who were big enough to help. Fathers and mothers worked together raising crops and caring for animals, although perhaps working on different aspects of those jobs.[9] Mothers raised the children, but fathers were nearby and pitched in.

Then, as massive technological changes altered the structure of societies all over the world and brought automobiles, indoor plumbing, and industrial growth— for which I give thanks every time I do the laundry (it's a lot better than beating clothes with rocks at the river-bank)—the jobs created by new technologies required specialization. This proved disruptive to families. By

---

7. Harriett H. Arrington, "Alice Merrill Horne: Arts Promoter and Early Utah Legislator," in *Worth Their Salt: Notable but Often Unnoted Women of Utah*, ed. Colleen Whitley (Logan: Utah State University Press, 1996), 177–88.

8. Kylie Turley, "Kanab's All Woman Town Council, 1912–1914: Politics, Power Struggles, and Polygamy," *Utah Historical Quarterly* 73, no. 3 (summer 2005): 308–28.

9. The duality of jobs was reflected in, for example, men working on the "shear side," shearing wool from sheep, and women on the "distaff side," the distaff being the rotating shaft holding wool at the spinning wheel.

the late 1940s and into the 1950s, fathers felt compelled to leave their homes in search of work; mothers felt the need to stay home with the children. As I see it, the fundamental shifts in attitudes during that period came from three factors:

First, in the city, one person—the father in nearly every instance[10]—had to commute to work, leaving the children with the mother.

Second, the new jobs required higher education and a period of training as an apprentice/journeyman, that kind of thing. Since girls were expected to marry and become pregnant, boys were the ones who were chosen to go to college or to a training school. Often the jobs required great physical strength, which favored men, and even if specific women were stronger than specific men, the perception of strength gave men the edge.

The third and most significant factor, however, was the emerging tradition that the business world was made for men, so that when Eugene Meyer retired from the *Washington Post* in 1946, he passed the baton to his son-in-law, Philip Graham, rather than to his daughter, Katherine. When Philip died in 1963, the world had changed enough that Katherine was able to assume the paper's leadership and do well running the company,

10. In 1963 I taught with a woman whose husband had become an invalid, so she became the sole support of the family. She was ineligible for the benefits granted to male personnel, such as the normal "dependency allowance" for children.

even in the face of lingering criticism about a woman being put in charge of such an enterprise.[11]

Industrialization created the need for women to stay at home because there were few options for child care. The rising medium of television featured shows like *Father Knows Best* (1949–1954), and there were many companies that would not even consider hiring women—nor would they hire racial or ethnic minorities—for anything beyond basic entry-level jobs, for which the employees were paid far less than the men who did exactly the same work.[12] Similarly, insurance companies offered radically different coverage for men and women and some refused to cover children if the policy was on the mother.

Consequently, the idea grew among Mormons as well as others that men belonged in the marketplace and women should stay at home. The altered perceptions made the world I grew up in different from what my Mormon ancestors had known. When I graduated from high

11. It is still big news when a woman becomes CEO of a company, and whether a female CEO is allowed to play at the Augusta Golf Course still causes a stir. In the 1960s–70s, the courts had to compel the Elks and Lions Clubs to include women.

12. Forty-odd years ago, one of the men on the faculty where I taught told me he had taken an assembly-line summer job to earn money for college. He had earned more than the women on the assembly line who had been there for years and were better at their work than he was. Men, he learned, had to be paid a given amount due to union negotiations, but the rate for women was left up to the company. He was also told that in the fall he would be replaced by two or three women for the same budgetary allowance.

school in 1958, women could aspire to three occupations besides clerking in a store, waiting tables, or working on an industrial line: nursing, secretarial work, or teaching. To be completely fair, the implied discrimination worked both ways because men who wanted to be nurses, secretaries, or elementary-school teachers were impeded too; the suspicions people had about their manhood were voiced loudly and not necessarily very nicely.[13]

I had a roommate in college at the University of Utah in 1961 who was majoring in interior design. That was an okay major for a woman intending to become a clerk in a fabric store. As part of her major, she had to take a drafting class in the architecture department. As the only female in the class, she was singled out with contempt by the professor as he greeted the students every day with, "Good morning, gentlemen, *and you*," the last part said with theatrical emphasis. She was determined to earn the highest grade in the class to show the teacher what a woman could do. She fell short of that goal but scored near the top on every test, albeit without winning over the professor, who still thought she didn't belong there.

I majored in education after I received a Utah State Normal scholarship to cover my tuition for four years. I

---

13. When prospective teachers were first given the Minnesota Multiphasic Personality test, it included such questions as whether the subject would "rather play football or read a book," resulting in the impression that a surprising number of homosexuals planned to go into teaching. A normal man, it was assumed, would prefer football.

wanted to study law and thought I would, after I filled the requirement of my scholarship and taught for two years. I realized, however, that the highest I could probably achieve at a law firm would be to work as a clerk. Something else I hadn't counted on was how much I would enjoy teaching English to ninth graders in the Weber County School District. I loved it.

After that, I pursued a graduate degree in English literature at Brigham Young University. Because the school was growing sharply, the department needed to hire several new teachers and decided on Neal Lambert, Steven Walker, and me. Both Neal and Steve would go on to full-time careers at the school. The decision to hire me was unusual for the day; few universities hired women as full-time faculty. When the semester ended and I married Tom Whitley, I found out just how unusual my situation was when I learned that my faculty health insurance would not cover my spouse, even though male teachers' insurance covered their entire families. In addition, I was told I could not have a faculty parking permit because I had a student husband. Nor would my husband be allowed to take classes for free as the wives of male faculty did. If that was not enough, I was also told I would not be retained permanently because I was of child-bearing age.

That Christmas another woman on the English faculty, whom I will call Pam, got married. After winter semester started, Soren Cox, who had been my supervisor as a graduate assistant, called me into his office and said my name would be "bandied about a bit in the next few weeks" as he and other men in the English Department, to their credit, challenged the university's policies regarding women. He said he had watched helplessly as the department had lost good teachers simply because they had gotten married. The men who took this on had been looking for a means of protest and had decided to focus their arguments to two restrictive practices they thought they could overturn. My case was cited to show the injustice of the benefits issues, while Pam's case was intended to highlight the right of a woman to continue working after marrying. As a result of the push-back in these two areas, the benefits policies were changed—not in time for us, of course, but it did eventually help Tom's sister, Jan. When she was hired to assist Ernest Wilkinson in writing a history of BYU, she was given insurance coverage for her husband and he was allowed a family reduction in tuition.

The right to continue working was different. Pam had been chosen because she had physical problems that, for the time being, prevented her from becoming pregnant. I vividly remember her returning from an interview with the school's president, saying she had "just had the kind of conversation with President Wilkinson I usually reserve for my gynecologist." She said she would stay another year but added, "I'm not going through that again." The rule against hiring married women stayed in place for several years. It was the same elsewhere in academia and the business world, these rights being won slowly and in some instances only after court battles.

Some women in business kept their maiden names to conceal the fact that they had gotten married, which worked until a woman became pregnant. In those days application forms often asked a woman when her last menstrual period had been, and I always wrote my answer as sloppily as I could in protest of such an inappropriate question. Discouraged by these policies, and not able to see the possibility of university employment in the future, I decided not to pursue a doctoral degree.

Instead, I taught reading and high school equivalency classes to young men seventeen to twenty-one years old, from inner-city ghettos and the rural Old South, who were entering the Job Corps.[14] I also helped develop a Salt Lake City school to train welfare recipients for new jobs and support them in gaining a high school diploma. All the while, I was watching the growing women's movement take on everything from job

---

14. For one young man from rural Illinois, school was too far away, but church was accessible. As the minister preached, the boy would follow along in his Bible, learning to read only with a preacher's cadence: "And Sam (rising inflection) said to Ann (falling inflection) where is Nip the dog (sharp rise) and Tab the cat (falling inflection)?" I never laughed—at least not out loud.

discrimination to spouse abuse. It came on the wave of the civil rights marches of the early 1960s,[15] but the shrillness of the message increased as women's rights advocates joined forces with the opposition to the Vietnam War and other causes. Some of the marches and sit-ins, where the young people lacked the cohesive moral core or careful training in the passive resistance of the Civil Rights Movement, turned ugly. These were played on the television news alongside scenes from the war.[16] The image of the women's liberation movement turned sour for many middle-class people.

Perhaps more significant was the concomitant issue of birth control and the related "free love" movement of the 1970s. Many people involved in the women's movement were advocating the abandonment of marriage as an outdated institution and for accepting sex as an

15. The twentieth-century women's liberation movement could be seen as beginning with Simone de Beauvoir's *The Second Sex* in 1954. However, the more obvious impetus for 1960s activism was Betty Friedan's *The Feminine Mystique*, published in 1963. The Equal Pay Act of 1963 and Title VII of the Civil Rights Act of 1964 placed women on a theoretical equal footing with men.

16. During the summer of 1967, race riots erupted in more than 100 American cities, the one in Newark lasting six days and leaving 26 people dead, 1,500 injured. In Detroit a week-long riot ended with 43 killed and 2,000 injured, as well as 5,000 homeless. The violence was quelled when President Lyndon Johnson sent in nearly 5,000 army paratroopers, but the root problems have still not been solved. See David Colburt, ed., *Eyewitness to America* (New York: Pantheon, 1997); Nick Kotz, *Judgment Days: Lyndon Baines Johnson, Martin Luther King Jr., and the Law That Changed America* (Boston: Houghton Mifflin, 2005).

interesting pastime. Combined with the stridency and extreme language employed by some feminists, this part of the movement offended those who had traditional views but who may have otherwise become advocates for women's rights. Certainly women's liberation did not gain a lot of friends among the LDS membership during that time. In the 1980s the church took a stand against the Equal Rights Amendment, partly because of feminism's negative image and partly because the amendment could be interpreted in ways that might be detrimental to women, prohibiting divorced wives from receiving alimony, for instance.[17] In any case, the lines hardened between those who thought women should be able to choose for themselves regarding a career and those who felt mothers should stay home with their children. In 1971 when I became pregnant, I decided to stay home with my son. That drew praise from some acquaintances,

17. I attended the ERA conference in Salt Lake City with several other members of our stake Relief Society board. We found several LDS men in attendance working the crowd in opposition to the amendment. Only later did we learn that they had earlier called women and claimed to represent the church so they could hold meetings on church property. When the church's general authorities learned of their actions, they issued a statement specifically prohibiting the use of church property for any political activities except as polling places. The key session was chaired by Esther Landa, a Jewish woman who had been a force for good in Utah government and charities for years. She held the more strident elements in the room in check with her gentle, kind, judicial demeanor, which earned applause from the entire audience.

condolences from others, and outright criticism from a few, but since it was based on answers to my own and my husband's prayers, I ignored the commentary of others. Nonetheless, when I eventually returned to teach at BYU nineteen years later,[18] I mentally punched the air and yelled *Yes!* every time I saw one of the Honors deans carry her baby into her office.

The variety of jobs I took while waiting and hoping to have children helped me see that discrimination exists in more than one form and that all these injustices are interwoven, that we have to work on each of them in order to untangle the giant knot. I could also see the attitude of the LDS Church changing, and in some cases the church's response to issues was far quicker and much more sensible than that of other organizations, largely because the church's structure allows for personal interaction at the street level with bishops, Relief Society leaders, and others. For instance, as a ward-level Relief Society president myself, I told an abused wife to read Germaine Greer, a prominent feminist—and my bishop backed me up on it.[19]

---

18. I stayed home for several years, and considering the events that ensued—accidents and illnesses in our extended families, some predators in our neighborhood schools—it was a good thing I was home to help deal with them. When I was ready to return and felt the assurance through prayer that it was the right choice, I was offered a position within weeks.

19. Greer argued that a woman doesn't need to have a man

Like my bishop, other church leaders recognized that while we emphasize the family and encourage keeping families together, sometimes it is not for the best. The church gives support to the YWCA Shelter for Battered Women and Children in Salt Lake City.[20] It has called humanitarian service specialists in the church's wards and stakes to help individuals find work after divorce and other stressful situations. Last year, while I was working as an election judge, I met a lovely woman who had left her abusive husband on the advice of two bishops.

All of this, of course, reflects my experience in Utah. The church has had to adapt to cultural norms in other areas of the world. We think of dresses and skirts as appropriate church attire for women in this country, but in Vietnam it would be regarded as immodest because women wear pants there. That required some adjustment in thinking for the rest of us, but as an organization, as well as individually, we have managed to

in her life to be worthwhile. Her 1970 book, *The Female Eunuch*, was followed by several other books dealing with male dominance. See Christine Wallace, *Germaine Greer: Untamed Shrew* (New York: Faber & Faber, 1999). The young mother I advised took time out to orient her life, divorced her husband, remained a single mom for several years—with great support from the ward—regained her self-confidence and then entered a successful marriage.

20. One of the truly needed and positive outcomes of the liberation movement has been the establishment of shelters. Haven House was the first modern establishment of this type, opened in Pasadena in 1964. See "Haven House," *Women's Shelters: A Nationwide Directory of Shelters for Women*, womenshelters.org.

adapt to such cultural differences. I have great faith that we can continue to adjust our attitudes as the church spreads even more.

The crucial fact remains that we need to have personal space in which we can make decisions. We need to look beyond ourselves to see where we can be of help to people in other places, as well as in our own neighborhoods where women need assistance in choosing options suited to their particular circumstances. As a member of the church, I've been a counselor and president in both ward and stake organizations for adults, young adults, and children. I've taught classes for three-year-olds. I was a Boy Scout advancement chair for seventeen years. I have been a member of the activities committee, a family history consultant. I have sat on a lot of church councils where there was never a question about the equality of everyone in the room. I've also been an active member of the PTA, served as a member of community councils, and campaigned for candidates whose causes I felt were important. I have worked with dozens of government and civic organizations where I have not always felt that I was treated equally.

The fundamental premise of the gospel is that God loves each of us. He will guide us, and speak to us, no matter where we live or what gender we are. That does not mean we must simply accept everything in the world as it is. I think God expects us to do whatever we can to help

Colleen Whitley

ourselves and our brothers and sisters—which is to say, every other human being on the planet—wherever they live and whatever their status. Sometimes we do that quietly with no one else ever knowing about it and sometimes we have to fight a public, often noisy and unpleasant, battle. Whatever we do, we know our sisters can be among our strongest allies.

2 | Love Your Intellect

Erika Ball

I dread people asking what my profession is because most of the time it's a conversation killer. There are three ways the conversation plays out:

> Me: "I'm a statistician."
> Jane: "I took a statistics class once. I hated it."
> Me: *And wasn't that a delightful conversation?*

> Me: "I do statistics."
> Jane: "I loved my statistics class!"
> Me: *A fellow nerd!*

> Me: "Statistics."
> Jane: "What's that?"
> Me: "I work with math."
> Jane: "Oh, you're one of those smart ones."
> Me: *Time to change the topic. Any topic will do.*

The last response is particularly distressing, not because Jane doesn't know what a statistician is but because she equates math ability with being smart.

Somewhere in history, Western society got tied up in

the notion that to be smart is to be academically or analytically able, particularly in mathematical or verbal areas. As if this is not limiting enough, a second way we have restricted intelligence is by divvying up the mathematical and verbal goods, so to speak, apportioning one-half to males and the other half to females. The way the myth goes is that boys are better at math and reasoning. They are rational, intellectual, and logical. Girls do better in the arts and humanities. They are better at communicating, caring, and expressing themselves. Debunked many times, this myth still permeates our way of thinking. A third popular persuasion limiting our idea of intelligence is that faith and science are mutually exclusive and people of intellect cannot be persons of faith. Then there is the fourth argument echoing in our own minds, which is perhaps the most limiting of all: the argument that some people were born smart and we were not.

Each of these ideas distorts our view of intelligence to the point that we cannot recognize ability or its potential when we see it. These self-imposed limitations cause me to picture a whale-boned corset tightened around our collective consciousness, forcing individual differences into a standard form, petite and shapely. Instead of questioning why we have a corset at all, we suck in our collective breath and cinch the strings tighter. Well, I for one am tired of looking like an intellectual hourglass. The truth is that I am smart in many different ways. I am a woman and I do math. I believe in God and I am a scientist. I can choose to be more than I am now. It's time to loosen the lacings, to step out of the antiquated caging of the mind and feel free to be intelligent.

Broadening the Concept of Intelligence

Ask ten people what intelligence is and you will probably get as many answers: the ability to solve problems, clarity of thought, mental quickness, the ability to create a product or offer services. In some cultures, the concept of intelligence encompasses practical sense and societal responsibility.[1] I contend that people can be smart in all sorts of ways: street-smart; business-minded, emotionally mature; witty or clever; and even devious, manipulative, or criminal. Howard Gardner[2] broadened the traditional view of mental capacity to include these areas of ability:

- linguistic (verbalizing and communicating)
- logical-mathematical (reasoning and analyzing)
- musical (composing or facilitating music)
- bodily-kinesthetic (controlling one's body)
- spatial (visualizing)
- interpersonal (relating to people)

1. Etienne Benson, "Intelligence across Cultures," *Monitor on Psychology* 34, no. 2 (2003): 56, online at "Browse Monitor on Psychology Archive," *American Psychological Association*, www.apa.org/monitor/browse.aspx.

2. Howard Gardner, *Intelligence Reframed: Multiple Intelligences for the Twenty-first Century* (New York: Basic Books, 1999).

- intrapersonal (evaluating oneself)
- naturalistic (understanding nature)
- existential (comprehending things beyond
  sensory data)

Gardner's list, or any list that claims to enumerate all natural intelligences, is too short for my liking, even though I do appreciate his broader view of intelligence than society currently embraces.

Another societal paradigm I would overturn if I could is the way people are labeled intelligent only if their ability is superior to other people's. I often succumb to this way of thinking. For instance, while considering Gardner's list, I hesitated to apply the label *smart* to my musical abilities. I play the piano, but I lack the talent of those who are truly gifted. I can sing, but not as a virtuoso. Still, I decided I am music-smart. It is hard for me to write that naked statement without any of the modesty wrappers we usually apply, such as *fairly*, *reasonably*, or *pretty good*. Society says otherwise, that I am not smart relative to those who are the best in that field. But I believe any ability can be recognized and celebrated.

Intelligence exists along a spectrum. In LDS scripture, Abraham was taught that between "two spirits, one [will be] more intelligent than the other."[3] Implicit in this, as I read it, is that both beings are intelligent and the baseline is zero, not some arbitrary level based on

3. Abr. 3:18.

others' abilities. If zero ability is at one end, God's ability is at the other. In the same scriptural passage, God says, "I am the Lord thy God, I am more intelligent than they all." In comparison to Him, all of us are infants—even though God perceives intelligence in us more freely than we do in each other.

Loosening the lacings on the corset and expanding our view of intelligence on these two points alone, academic ability and how we compare our intelligence to that of other people, restores oxygen and makes us feel we can breathe more deeply the experiences of life.

Shedding Gender-Intelligence Stereotypes

The real physical corsets of antiquity were worn by women who wanted to achieve an hourglass figure because it was considered ideal in their societies. In our day, we have shed our physical corsets to accept various physical shapes, but we live under persistent gender-defined stereotypes that restrict our progress as women in math and science. The idea that women are not as logical and reasonable as men has been proven to be a farce. The most convincing arguments show there is no biological difference in intelligence between males and females.[4] I

---

4. "'Women Worse at Math Than Men' Explanation Scientifically Incorrect, Experts Say," *Science Daily*, Jan. 18, 2012, online at www.sciencedaily.com; Jonathan M. Kane and Janet E. Mertz, "Debunking Myths about Gender and Mathematics Performance," *Notices of the American Mathematical Society* 59, no. 1 (Jan. 2012), 10–21.

concede that there is a disparity in the number of women versus men in some fields of science, technology, engineering, and math (STEM), but it is not because of a lack of *biological capacity*. When society finally realized that women were under-represented in these areas, all sorts of initiatives were invented to encourage women to enter them. I was exposed to a variety of technical fields as I participated in a program in the 1990s that let women look through an electron microscope, dissect a shark, listen to commentaries on whether a Jurassic Park would be feasible, build reflector ovens to cook hot dogs, talk about the commutability of diseases, explore the nascent World Wide Web, and gather data to evaluate the effectiveness of shampoos. I already loved math and needed little convincing to pursue a career in STEM, but the program did help me see the application and potential of my education.

I ended up in one of the few professions in the STEM universe that already boasted female participation: women have been involved in statistics for nearly as long as the field has existed. One of the earliest and most recognizable statisticians was, in fact, Florence Nightingale, who gathered data and determined that poor sanitation lay behind the high death rates during her time. While I am hardly a pioneer in my field, I feel somewhat involved in disproving the gender stereotype because I am a woman doing math, embracing my intellectual figure for what it is.

Accepting That Faith and Reason Can Co-exist

Part of accepting my own intelligence has involved embracing my inner nerd. I own a red statistics t-shirt that says, "Without data, you're just another person with an opinion." I wore this shirt on a trip, and an older gentleman at the airport complimented me on it. I smiled and laughed. He boarded before me, and I soon saw that he would be my seat companion. After introducing ourselves, he enquired why I was visiting Washington, DC (business), what kind of family I had (two brothers, one sister, parents still happily married), where I grew up (Phoenix), and where I went to school (BYU). This led him to ask if I was Mormon. He had never met a member of our faith before and wanted to know what we believed. He offered that he himself was agnostic. The trickiest question he asked was this: "So you're a scientist *and* you believe in God and an afterlife. That seems like a contradiction. How do you reconcile that?"

I shared the only thing that came to mind at the moment, the phrase from the Doctrine and Covenants that we believe in seeking learning "by study and also by faith."[5] His face showed skepticism as he mulled over the idea for a moment, and then we moved on to another topic. That got me thinking about my faith. I had never perceived a contradiction, and I certainly didn't feel like my scientific

---

5. Doctrine and Covenants, 88:118.

side and my spiritual side were at war. I concluded three things: (1) I am strongly influenced by evidence; (2) I believe that evidence can be obtained by more than just five senses, that what we *feel* inside can constitute evidence; and (3) faith and analytical reasoning can co-exist. Faith does not dampen or weaken my reasoning, and in some ways, it augments my analytical conclusions. What I really need, I concluded, is a shirt that says, "Without faith, you're just another person with data."

One of the things I appreciate about my faith is that it gives me a reason to seek knowledge. I pursue knowledge and learning that I may better understand and serve others. When illness affects a friend, educating myself about their condition allows me to provide better emotional and physical support than otherwise. When voices in the political sphere seek to silence my religious voice, learning about my right to speak and vote according to my conscience gives me confidence to act on and assert those rights. Scripture teaches me that "whatever principle of intelligence we attain unto in this life, it will rise with us in the resurrection."[6] I find in these words a security similar to that of having an external backup for my computer. It assures me that when my drive eventually crashes, years of thought and work will not be lost, dissipated into the universe. All of this knowledge is

---

6. Ibid., 130:18.

important to amass and maintain because I want to be like God, whose glory is intelligence.[7] Thus my faith encourages my learning and enhances my intellect.

The areas of life the gentleman on the airplane found incompatible, faith and intellect, can work synergistically, my intellect helping to deepen my faith and stimulate my gospel scholarship. For example, I've learned that the etymology of *intelligence* comes from the Latin roots *inter* (between) and *legere* (to read or choose).[8] In other words, the literal meaning might be "to choose between." This is interesting when applied to the scriptural passage in which Abraham described his view of the premortal world and called the nascent spirits "intelligences."[9] Those souls were endowed with power to choose between alternate plans and alternate leadership models. We can similarly choose here on earth, as intelligent beings in the most fundamental sense of the word. Insights like these illustrate how I gain more by marrying my faith and intellect rather than by separating or compartmentalizing the two.

It is liberating, to let myself be both a woman of faith and a woman of intelligence. I give you the same permission, if you need it: don't let someone else define your faith or your intelligence or tell you your faith is

7. Ibid., 93:36.

8. *Online Etymology Dictionary*, s.v. "intelligence."

9. Abr. 3:22.

somehow different and distinct from your intelligence. Such assumptions are a disservice.

Accepting Our Intelligence

Shunning society's views of intelligence only gets us so far. We also have to confront the personal doubt that tells us the same, that we are not as smart as everybody else. I believe that belittling our intelligence is as damaging to the psyche as disparaging our bodies. As a parallel to the Love Your Body campaign, which encourages people to reject advertising ideals, I propose a similar movement to Love Your Intellect. Its tenets would be simple: recognize that there are different types of intelligence, all of which are beautiful and important; seek for self-improvement in areas of personal interest; and appreciate your abilities at whatever level you enjoy them.

I have already addressed the idea of a broadened view of intelligence. I invite you to take a minute to consider the people in your life you admire. Do some of them have a special knack for gardening? If so, we should be grateful for the beauty and food these people can coax from the ground. Do you know people who are whiz-zes at designing, fixing, and engineering? Do you have friends who pick you up emotionally by saying just what you need to hear? I do, and my life is greatly enriched by their abilities.

When I consider the strengths people have, it is

easy to compare myself to them and realize how subpar I am by comparison. Recognizing my weaknesses is probably beneficial as long as I don't dwell on them. If you are as self-critical as I am, you have your list of personal weaknesses memorized. Let's change that thinking and consider that these are areas where we have opportunities to improve. The beauty of life is that we are not consigned to remain in our current state of being forever; we can change if we want to. We can become smarter tomorrow than we are now. We can choose an area of improvement and work on it today. We have all eternity to develop, so there is no need to fret about all our deficiencies if we work at them one opportunity at a time.

We should, of course, ask what we are good at. It might take time to identify strengths, but in doing so we should give ourselves honest credit. Ask yourself if you are the one who knows how to keep family relationships running smoothly. Do you serve your nation or community in civic roles? Do you have artistic or practical skills? Have you figured out the most efficient way to feed children, clean them, read to them, and put them to bed? If so, you are a success in that area and should accept it.

Society's views will continue to bear many of the distortions caused by the imaginary corset, but as individuals we can shed that caging. We can expand our views and free ourselves from gender stereotypes. We can believe that reason and faith can co-exist. We can appreciate the different types of talent people have in areas outside of academia: at home, in business, and in the studio or garden. At first the figure in the mirror seems unfamiliar and slightly bulbous in its intellectual form. But after a moment of self-doubt, I have been able to accept my aptitudes and abilities and declare to the world, "I am intelligent. I love my intellect!" And that self-embrace has been the most liberating of all.

3 | Career Mother

Rachael Decker Bailey

"I don't want to be a mommy when I grow up. Do I have to?"

The question catches me off guard, and I look into the rearview mirror. Five solemn little faces with my own eyes look back at me. The questioner is my nine-year-old, who has caused me endless soul-searching, who has posed questions in her short life that I've always shied away from asking myself in my thirty-one years.

I struggle with my own inclinations versus the answer I feel I should give, the answer that's in accordance with my beliefs and my life choices. I firmly believe, both from my upbringing and from my own experience, that women are filled with boundless potential and the capacity to succeed in both the academic realm and in the workplace; but on the other hand, my diplomas reside at the bottom of a box underneath a stack of children's crafting supplies. And even though I think of myself as a stay-at-home mother, the truth is that I'm on the books as part-time faculty at the local university. I want my daughters to educate themselves, to receive graduate degrees, to have the ability and training to support themselves and their families—but I also want them to understand that they are my greatest accomplishment, and I want them to feel the same way about their future children. How do I appropriately convey this mixed bag of difficult emotional choices and ongoing trial and error to my young daughter?

While I engage in brief but furious internal turmoil, the cars in front of us moving down the hill, I accelerate as my younger daughter chimes in. "I don't want to be a mommy either," she says. "I don't want to get married!" They giggle, then lean forward, waiting for my response to this daring statement.

"When I was your age, I didn't want to be a mommy either," I respond slowly. "And I didn't want to get married. I wanted to do a lot of other things and have an exciting job. And then I met Daddy and decided it would be really fun to be married, if I was married to him."

Both girls nod enthusiastically at the mention of their father, who is by far their favorite. He is the fun one, the one who tosses them in the air and pushes them (too high) on the swings and takes them to the pool and feeds them popsicles in the bathtub while he reads aloud from *The Hobbit*. I am the disciplinarian, the one who reminds everyone to pack their lunches, to put away their laundry, the one who checks over the completed homework. My agony over this duality has resulted in a conscious effort to become a "fun parent," something that does not come naturally to my checklist-prone mind. When we sit in the afternoon sunshine with a pile of picture books, I close my eyes as I inhale the sweet fragrance of their Johnson & Johnson–scented hair, praying that this is the mother they will remember when they look back on their childhoods rather than the one who was quietly questioning herself in her struggle to find a balance: the woman who is walking the fence that separates her family's needs and her own sense of self.

"And then," I say slowly, "Daddy and I decided that we wanted to have a family that was part of both of us, that we wanted to have you, and so I became a mommy. I still do other things, though," I remind them, pointing out the window as we drive past the university. "I teach there, remember?"

"Oh yeah … I forgot," says my oldest, screwing up her face thoughtfully.

I turn on my left blinker. "Can I tell you a secret?" I ask, changing lanes. My girls lean forward eagerly.

"I used to really like teaching, but now I like being a mother better. When I teach I have to do boring things like grade papers and tell people they didn't turn in their homework. As a mother, I do cool stuff like read stories all morning and go to the zoo and color pictures."

I don't mention the less-glamorous underbelly

involving endless laundry and piles of dishes and runny noses, the daily realities that comprise my hamster wheel. What I determinedly focus on—and it's a conscious choice I sometimes cling to with gritted teeth—is the idea that I love this, that I chose it, that this is what will bring me the greatest long-term joy.

"Oh," says my daughter. And with the charming inconsistency of childhood, she changes the subject completely, and I don't pursue it further. We pull up to the dance studio where I escort her inside, kiss her goodbye, and return to the car to take my younger children to the library.

My husband and I met sitting next to each other in a class just after his mission at the beginning of my sophomore year at BYU. We married a few months after finals. I was nineteen, he had just turned twenty-two. I quickly found myself in a strange limbo. While many of the other young wives I knew had dropped out to put their husbands through school, I continued on. My friends in graduate school a few years later were mostly unmarried, while I was bouncing a baby in my lap during conferences with students.

When we decided to have children, it was simply the next achievement in a long string of trophies and glowing report cards. We had been married for two years; I was starting grad school and everyone in our student ward was having babies. Living in Provo, it seemed like the logical step. I was young enough that my worldview consisted of making a plan, working to achieve it, and voila! Success. I was convinced that hard work would always bring me happiness and gratification commensurate with my level of effort. Children, I thought, would be no different. We decided it would be perfect timing to have our first baby born after my first year of graduate school. As I had come to expect from my life, things went just as I'd planned them with the arrival of our first child the week after final exams.

But pregnancy and motherhood blindsided me. I felt like my brain had been stuffed with cotton wool and there was a disconnect between my brain and my mouth. When I sat in class, struggling to coalesce my thoughts, I imagined a web of frail synapses that didn't quite line up, ends frayed into tendrils waving futilely next to one another. My twenty-four-hour, chemically induced labor lived up to the ghoulish horror stories told by my sisters-in-law. Just weeks after giving birth, we moved so my husband could complete a summer internship in a tiny resort town, and I spent that summer lying on a couch eating chocolate chips, reading Agatha Christie mysteries, and crying whenever the baby cried. I viewed my return to graduate school in the fall as my salvation. I refused to think about what would happen when I finished my degree the following spring.

After my graduation, we moved across the country so my husband could begin a doctoral program at Purdue

University. I had a year-old baby whom I absolutely adored, but I hated the fact that she practically lived in her stroller while my husband and I traded her back and forth all day between classes. I wanted her friends to be other babies, not the twenty-year-olds in the TA lab who thought she was cute. With the memory of the previous summer fresh in my mind, I knew I *wanted* to learn to love the life of a mother, to find things I enjoyed about it, and to develop friendships with other mothers rather than sitting dumbly in the corner during playgroups. I was determined to be happy.

To achieve this goal, I realized, I would need to seek out activities and methodologies that made me feel like a Successful Mother. In our new home, my first purchase was a bike with a child seat; I tentatively asked a few women at church if they'd be interested in biking to the playground with us. Before I knew it, we had a twice-weekly date and I was eagerly learning from the other mothers about napping schedules and solid foods and the best library storytimes. I sought out women who were thrilled to be mothers, and I soaked up everything I could from them. It was a summer opposite in every way to the one before it. I was exuberantly joyful in my daughter's company rather than dreading my husband's departure for work each morning. And unlike the previous year, I was reluctant to return to the university that fall.

Although I had accepted a teaching position with

Purdue, I chose not to continue my own education. As much as I felt I *should* want to earn a doctorate, when I prayed about it the answer was clear: that was not my path. The fallout was dismal. I'd been awarded the department's premier graduate student recognition, and there were professors who were unrestrained when they expressed shock that I was planning to "let my brain rot away in the service of an infant," as one of them put it. Her sentiments echoed my own private ones at the time. What, I asked in my prayers, was the point of all those years of 4.0 GPAs, publications, and professional networking? When I evaluated the things I was good at, none of them seemed remotely relevant to motherhood. The only rationale I could offer, both to my professors and to myself, was that I felt strongly that it was the path I should take. I would teach a class for one year, I thought, and that would gradually allow me to slip into my new role as a stay-at-home mother away from academia.

Nine years and another four babies later, I am still teaching two advanced writing classes every semester at Purdue. After my third child was born, I told the department I was leaving. They offered me the chance to teach online instead. Teaching online (and the flexibility to grade papers and answer e-mails in my pajamas) resulted in such a separation of my academic career from my mental self-image that it's always a bit of a shock when someone asks casually how my classes are going.

I determinedly think of myself as a *career mother* now, a term I coined during an interview about food preservation with the local newspaper. I took an instant dislike to the overdressed reporter who brushed invisible specks from her tailored skirt while directing her photographer to snap photos of my pantry. It was filled with rows of glass jars, their contents the product of hours of labor in a garden and in the steam-filled air of my sunny autumn kitchen. She turned to look at me where I was perched on a table, a cherubic baby on my lap and another long-lashed toddler peeping out from behind my arm.

"You have two children?" she said, arching one over-plucked brow.

"Five, actually," I replied, pressing a kiss on the top of my baby's curly head. Her eyebrows lifted and she exchanged a meaningful look with her photographer.

"My," she said. "Quite a family."

"Quite a blessing," I responded, a touch acerbically. "I think of myself as a career mother," I said. "I'm raising children, not just vegetables."

This idea of being a career mother is a pet notion of mine. It implies that this is my choice, not that I just fell into it by default. In her book *The Happiness Project*, Gretchen Rubin counsels readers to "act the way you want to feel."[1] That is what, in many ways, I am doing.

---

1. Gretchen Rubin, *The Happiness Project: Or Why I Spent a Year*

Seeing myself as a career mother allows me to elevate what I do beyond the humdrum, beyond the minutiae of housekeeping and lunch packing. *Career mother* embodies all of the consuming mental effort that goes into creating a home environment that is nurturing and sacred. It underscores a woman's deliberate choice to turn her considerable education and skills toward her family rather than sacrifice herself on the altar of the mundane as a long-suffering laundry martyr. It means doing the very best of which I am capable rather than the bare minimum needed to sustain life. It's being a homemaker, not a housekeeper. It reminds me that I am worthwhile, my education is valuable, and I am continuing as a career overachiever rather than giving up on myself. Perhaps, as one recent study found, this is how we convince ourselves that the high costs of parenting are worthwhile.[2] I, however, think that if I'm going to be a mother, I might as well try to be the best mother out there, one who is engaged, loving, and joyful.

One of the most valuable lessons I have learned, in addition to this label of career mother that I flaunt next to the "don't call me a housewife" chip on my shoulder, is that there is still a genuine need for separation between

Trying to Sing in the Morning, Clean My Closets, Fight Right, Read Aristotle, and Generally Have More Fun (New York: HarperCollins, 2009), 261.

2. "Parents Rationalize the Economic Cost of Children by Exaggerating Their Parental Joy," *Science Daily*, Mar. 2, 2011, citing the Association for Psychological Science, online at www.sciencedaily.com.

wife and motherhood and from the woman who retains other interests outside of those roles. The month after my second child was born, I took up running, primarily to escape a fussy baby for a few minutes at the end of a long day. I have always been fairly athletic, but long-distance running struck a deep chord within me and I've never looked back. There is something satisfying in the struggle to push myself harder every day, to shave off a few seconds from my previous day's time, to run headlong into the wind, to feel my stride eating up mile after mile, or to cross the finish line of my latest marathon. Running has taught me self-control and mental discipline. That, in turn, has enhanced my capability as a mother. I throw my medals into the back of my closet, but I constantly carry with me the lessons I've learned in winning them. Running makes me feel like I am someone unique, interesting, and successful in ways that are immediately visible. I am not just a mother, I am a marathon runner, and that is huge, vital—an essential component of my life that did not exist before my children were born. It supplies the positive reinforcement and measurable growth that I missed upon leaving academia.

Oddly enough, being a runner also gives me hope for my daughters and their eventual confrontation with the same dilemmas. I have stumbled—and am still stumbling—through the process of re-creating my identity as both a mother and as an individual. When

I found out my third, fourth, and fifth children would be boys, I was relieved to think they would be spared the heartache of choosing between the life advocated by their faith and the path cleared by their intellect. I feel more at peace with these questions now and trust that both my daughters and my sons will find their lives shaped and forged into something more challenging and ultimately more magnificent than anything they have imagined for themselves.

There has been no transcendent realization for me, no one moment when I learned to reconcile my divergent desires and yearnings. It has been a gradual process. There are fewer dark days of self-questioning now than there were five years ago. Even so, some days are good and some are not; sometimes my heart swells with gratitude for my perfect little family and sometimes I dissolve into tears and leave the dinner table. It has been a gradual process for me to make it this far, to be able to introduce myself as a mother of five children without immediately adding that I have a graduate degree and still teach. I have no wisdom to offer other than my own experience, hard-won and painful as it is.

My children are, quite simply, the delight of my life. They are my greatest source of worry and stress as well, but they are my delight. As I kiss my baby's fat cheeks and hear his delighted "Mamamama!"; tuck in my three-year-old and accede to his imperious demands to "Tiss me,

Mama!"; cuddle up with my five-year-old, who gently rubs his cheek against my shoulder as I read to him; or sit cross-legged on the floor across from my seven-year-old as she confesses to some minor peccadillo—this, right here, for me, is happiness. This is when I feel that great upswelling in my chest, that explosion of love and warmth and divine assurance that carries me onward. Purposefully seeking out these moments, then, and making a deliberate effort to create not only the moments but the kind of mothering life that I have told myself is enriching, productive, and worthwhile—perhaps this is as close to transcendence as I will come.

Glennon Melton beautifully characterized such experiences as "kairos moments":

> There are two different types of time. *Chronos* time is what we live in. It's regular time, it's one minute at a time, it's staring down the clock till bedtime time, it's ten excruciating minutes in the Target line time, it's four screaming minutes in time-out time, it's two hours till daddy gets home time. Chronos is the hard, slow passing time we parents often live in.
>
> Then there's *Kairos* time. Kairos is God's time. It's time outside of time. It's metaphysical time. It's those magical moments in which time stands still. I have a few of those moments each day. And I cherish them.[3]

---

3. Glennon Melton, "Don't Carpe Diem," *Huffington Post*, Jan. 14, 2012, online at "Parents," *Huff Post*, www.huffingtonpost.com.

When I first read Melton's essay, I was electrified. Finally someone was putting a name to those feelings I had worked so hard to actively create. A list maker by instinct, I decided to incorporate enriching items like storytime, thirty minutes of engaged playtime, and quality one-on-one time into my daily laminated to-do list, wedged in with the other bulleted tasks like laundry, vacuuming, cleaning the refrigerator, and writing thank-you notes. I need those idealized moments when I can look at my children running through sun-dappled woods ahead of me and think, "This right here, right now, is perfect." What I have learned, more than anything, is that happiness does not always come on its own—it, like career motherhood, is a choice. I cannot sit back and wait for bliss to wash over me. If I want to find joy in mothering, if I want to enjoy my career as a mother, I have to construct my life so that joyful moments are possible, likely, and frequent. Happiness takes work. This truth may seem paradoxical, but simply creating more time for walks in the woods and jettisoning the Play-Doh that I loathe has brought me infinite satisfaction.

Before my oldest child was two, I began blogging the wonderful, miraculous moments I was sometimes experiencing, the moments I wanted to pretend I was having all the time. A sidebar quote from *Elizabeth and Her German Garden* reminded me of the life I wanted to create: "What a happy woman I am living in a garden,

with books, babies, birds, and flowers, and plenty of lei-
sure to enjoy them!"[4] My posts have been dotted with
appreciation for the moments I would not have if I were
not a career mother—the day I found my toddler in her
crib without pants but still wearing her bulky slippers,
which made me laugh until my stomach hurt; getting a
hug from a pint-sized T-Rex with "some weewee sarp
cwaws, Mama!"; spending time reading aloud as we work
our way through a stack of picture books; and finding
leaves of baby spinach carefully stuck all over the fridge
with alphabet magnets. These are snapshots of the life
I am determinedly trying to create for my family—one
that is full of museum trips, walks in the woods, bread
fresh from the oven and slathered with homemade jam,
and watercolors on the back porch.

After nine years of graduate study, my husband is
finishing his doctoral program. On one occasion he
mentioned that he wished his program had been more
structured rather than based solely on his own research
goals. Benchmarks, he said, would have been nice. He
mused about how it would have been different had he
chosen medical or law school. As he spoke, I thought
about what I would do differently if I were to return to
school. Would I change my course of study and take up
finance? Interior design? Culinary arts? Exercise science?

---

4. Elizabeth Von Arnim, *Elizabeth and Her German Garden* (London:
Macmillan, 1898), 18.

I mentally sorted through the things I've found reason to feel passionate about since my graduation and realized that turning any of those into a job would take the joy out of them. Twelve hours on my feet in an overheated kitchen? Not so fun. The same goes for doing someone else's taxes or prescribing physical therapy exercises (having gone to physical therapy myself, it has to be one of the most mind-numbing ways I've ever seen someone put a doctoral degree to use). As I listened to my husband dissect different options, I realized that my current job is the only one that allows me to pursue all of the myriad things in which I'm interested.

We joke wryly about a mother's job being a composite of maid, chauffeur, chef, librarian, decorator, accountant, and laundress. But the truth is, I enjoy all of these roles. I may not enjoy all of them every day (teaching a child to use a fork is harder than I'd ever imagined), but I relish the freedom to dictate my own environment and create a place that reflects my values, tastes, and preferences. If I want to spend a day doing nothing but reading stories to my children, I can do it. If I want to spend a day scrubbing the house until it gleams, I can do that too. I love the life I am living. I still second-guess myself and cry and wish I could change some aspects of it, pray every night for more patience the next day, and stress over little things and big things, but I am happy nonetheless. I chose it, and I choose to love it.

The most important thing I have learned is that this *is* a choice. Becoming a mother—the act of giving birth that first time—is not the event that dramatically affected my life. Rather, *deciding* my children could be my greatest accomplishment if I made a conscious, deliberate, and determined effort to view motherhood as a gift, a blessing, a career, and a calling—that was my all-important choice. That is the choice I re-commit to every day. That is the one that has shaped me into the woman I am today: the woman who is finding joy in the journey, the woman who has ditched her daily planner full of assignments to complete in exchange for a pantry door covered by a list of memories to make.

4 | Mommy, Meet Karen

Karen Challis Critchfield

From a very early age, I remember giving up on childhood dreams for the sake of being a mother. I had thought of being an astronaut, a forest ranger, or a marine biologist, but each of those thoughts were pushed aside when I decided it would be difficult to have a family and a career of that type too. I'm not sure if it was indirectly taught or if I put the thought into my own head, but I came to believe it was my role, even my place, to be a wife and mom and that everything else should come second to motherhood. As I look back, I realize that over time I was slowly and methodically denying myself in an attempt to become the person I thought I was supposed to be. I assumed I would be perfectly happy raising children and did not plan anything beyond motherhood. Having children would be, in my sight, the pinnacle of my existence.

For the first few years of my marriage, I was the primary breadwinner. I worked a basic job to support my husband's education so he could ultimately take over the breadwinner's role and I would be able to raise our kids. Then my daughter was born. After the initial baby blues, everything felt perfect. For the first few months, I reveled in life; my little girl was everything to me. However, as time went on, I started to feel dragged down by my new routine. The few activities I used to enjoy at home, particularly cooking, lost their appeal.

Being a stay-at-home mom was not as easy and blissful as I had thought it would be. It consumed my time and yet was unsatisfying. I felt lonely, unfulfilled, and empty. I also felt terrible guilt. I had always believed motherhood would complete me, that I was meant to be happy as a mother, so I felt confused and angry with myself for not being satisfied with my role. How could I not be happy and fulfilled doing what I was supposed to do? I was not supposed to be bored spending time with my daughter, was I? She was wonderful, adorable, and perfect.

Despite her childlike perfection, I wanted to get away. I frequently found myself playing solitaire on the computer while Mina played. I watched too much television. I looked for reasons to go to the store simply to get out of the house; I often visited the same store three or four times a week to pick up random items. I began to understand why I knew so many women whose hobby was shopping. Whether for simple household goods or clothing, shopping was a way to escape the four walls of home. It brought that small, brief satisfaction that comes with exploring the world outside and obtaining something new. I otherwise felt trapped. I knew I had a problem, but I could not see a solution. Solitaire and other meaningless time killers seemed to be my only escape from the drudgery. I accepted it as my fate even though it depressed me. I was empty inside.

The emptiness started to affect my marriage. I brought less and less to the relationship with my husband, who would come home from work to a shell of a wife. I had nothing to discuss beyond what our daughter had done that day. In an attempt at conversation, I would tell him about all the chores I had done. He would never say it, and I don't think he could put his finger on it, but I became uninteresting to him.

During this time I had a conversation with a stranger who asked if I worked. I responded, "No, I'm just a stay-at-home mom." Even as the words came out of my mouth, I felt unsettled. I stewed over it for weeks in an attempt to pinpoint what had bothered me about it and came to realize it was because I was a stay-at-home mom and nothing else. I had lost touch with every other aspect of who I was. There was a time, years before, that if you had asked me to describe myself in one word, it would have been "passionate." I was the person who wanted to experience life to the fullest. At one time there had been a fire inside of me, but it had smoldered to the point that I no longer knew that person anymore.

For a while I thought the solution would be to dedicate myself more fully to my role as a mother, that I needed to be more passionate about that. I read parenting books and attempted to improve my mothering skills, but that wasn't filling my sense of emptiness: I still saw myself as a mother and nothing else. I had a few tearful conversations with my husband about this. I didn't want to change my role, and yet it clearly wasn't enough for me. There was more to who I was, buried somewhere within me. The problem was digging it out. I had to rediscover myself.

My husband was going to school and working. My daughter was learning to crawl, talk, walk, and I needed to be by her side. What was I exactly? I was a facilitator, not really accomplishing anything myself. I made meals, cleaned the house, did the laundry, and took care of my daughter—but those necessary chores were not stimulating most of the time, as they provided little room for growth or development. During nap time and the other brief moments I had to myself, I wasted the only opportunity I had to do something significant by watching television or surfing the web. That made me feel even more resentful about having to go back to my ordinary routine. I needed progress in some way, something to work toward.

Even though I had come to understand this need inside of me, I could not figure out how to get to where I wanted to be. I considered going back to school, but my husband was in school and we could not afford more tuition. I liked the idea of getting a part-time job, but I still wanted to be with my daughter. Admittedly, I blocked out some possible solutions due to how trapped I felt. Once I had decided to be a full-time mom, I was unable to open my mind to other alternatives.

Part of the answer to my dilemma came unexpectedly from a friend when she mentioned that she was working on her "101 in 1,001." Curious about that, I pressed her for more details. She said she had written a list of 101 goals for the next 1,001 days. I remember feeling a twinge of interest when I heard this. It seemed easy, and flexible enough that I could do it.

One afternoon as my daughter napped, I sat down at the computer and opened a new document. My mind was blank. Ironically, the only thing I could think about was having another baby. That was not what this was supposed to be about. Then I remembered a recipe I had been eyeing in one of my cookbooks. It was a complicated set of instructions for a ribbon sponge cake, requiring planning, a lot of time, and some equipment I didn't have. I had often looked fondly at the picture of the cake but had never contemplated making it because of the difficulty involved. Now, I thought, it was a perfect goal for me. I typed it in as number one on the list.

That is where my list stayed for several days. It was

not easy coming up with 101 goals, which had to be simple enough to accomplish alongside my baby and with limited funds, but which had to be real challenges. I wanted to include things I sincerely wanted to accomplish, that would help make me feel like a real person. Things that would bring me closer to knowing who I wanted to be. I began adding a few items related to motherhood, since that was such a core part of my life. I didn't want to stop being a mother, or even stop being a stay-at-home mother; I simply wanted to start being myself again in some way. I searched the Internet for lists with goals I never would have considered. As my own list grew, I began to feel a little excited about beginning. Some of the goals would be easy and only require that I devote enough time to completing them, while others were new and maybe slightly out of reach.

I started a blog and posted an entry entitled "Mommy, Meet Karen," with my list of goals and an explanation of why I was doing this. My first achievement was to create a new family tradition at Thanksgiving. I also started playing the piano again and re-learned some of my old recital pieces. I read the complete and unabridged version of *Moby Dick*. Some of the goals were memorable. Some were as simple as deciding to build a snowman with my daughter. I still think of that activity with Mina as one of the most wonderful days of my life. The remarkably soothing baking and cooking goals, including the completion of the ribbon sponge cake, revived the culinary interest I had lost and made some of the daily chores more bearable. Building strength enough to do ten pull-ups was surprisingly empowering. Riding a bike for the first time in a decade felt wonderful and made me feel like a kid again. Even completing the simplest of goals helped me learn a lot about myself as I discovered what I did and didn't like.

By far the most satisfying goal was hiking Mount Timpanogos. Many happy memories from my childhood involved hiking, and I wanted to rediscover that love. The feeling I had when I climbed to the top of the mountain was almost indescribable. It was as though a part of my soul had finally broken free of its cage. I cried with joy as I found that part of me that had been asleep for so long. I felt alive!

I have now completed my original list and am half-way through the second. To say that my 101 in 1,001 has been life-changing would be an understatement. I know that this is only a start toward discovering what my abilities are. Some days are still hard to get through, considering my household obligations, but I have made significant progress. As I work on my goals, I feel that old passion rekindling inside me.

My marriage has also improved. My husband has been a great support and encouraged me to complete my goals. We seem to be more open with each other now, and

I bring more to the conversation than talking only about children and chores. I have a little more to offer to the person I love; I think I am more like the person he originally fell in love with, the person I loved too.

I have just started to expand my own horizons, but I know that I am on the right path to being able to say I am more than "just a mom." I am also a baker, a hiker, a singer, a video gamer, a reader, and many other identities waiting to be discovered. But most importantly, I am Karen. I am enjoying the role of motherhood more because I am more at peace with being me.

As my good friend Jamie Zvirzdin wrote several years ago, "Don't put yourself on a shelf if you become a mother. You will need yourself more than ever." I have taken Karen off the shelf, dusted her off, and given her life again. My children deserve a mother who is real, someone with passions and interests. They deserve a relationship that goes beyond being cared for, one that can teach them that life has many dimensions.

For those women who may feel as I did, I encourage you to find yourself again. While creating a list of 101 goals is one path to self-discovery, it is certainly not the only way. Maybe such a list seems ambitious on the surface, but it comes down to the simplicity of making yourself matter. Don't sacrifice who you are for motherhood. Mommy, be you.

5 | Owning Our Spiritual Progress as Single Women

Carli Anderson

One of the most rewarding things about my life so far has been the unexpected amount of time I have spent as a single woman. I realize this may raise a few eyebrows, for many different reasons, but I can't help but state what is true. Being a single woman, even in a church of distinctly and divinely defined families, has turned out to be a source of more joy, adventure, self-awareness, contentment, and spiritual understanding than I would have guessed when I was dreamily planning out a very different life.

I suppose my early expectations couldn't be helped. We are, all of us, tightly bound to the forces that shape our aspirations, whether those forces are biological, cultural, or even theological. It's almost impossible not to plan a future based on expectations from at least one of these elements. In my case (as is probably true for most LDS women), I think it was all of the above. I never doubted my intrinsic worth in God's eyes. I knew that God viewed me as capable, important, and precious. I couldn't readily conceive of a path for myself that differed from the one my mother, grandmothers, and other women important to me had pursued.

You know the story. When biology, culture, and theology all converged upon an upper-twenty-something woman with no reasonable nuptial prospects, the effect wasn't especially pretty. There was distress, to be sure, and plenty of heartache. I constantly wondered what role I could play in a spiritual kingdom where families, and creating them, is a key theological function. What resulted was a genuine search for God's path for me, because I had no doubt that God had one.

A few more years and heartaches later, I have come to understand the value of womanhood more than I ever had before. Womanhood, regardless of marital status, is simply one of two manifestations of our child-of-God-hood, the "rich blessings" inherent to this state being completely inclusive and gender-neutral.[1]

The Myth of Lost Purpose

This sense of value can inadvertently slip through the cracks for those who find themselves outside the traditional cultural course for one reason or another. We women so often hear the characteristics of our own inner divinity and divine calling described in terms that

---

1. I am drawing from the lyrics to "I Am a Child of God," penned by Naomi W. Randall in 1957, included in the *Sing with Me* children's hymnal in 1969, and added to the LDS adult hymnal in 1985.

seem to imply a married, child-bearing role.[2] Combine that with the biological process within us, frequently described as some sort of ticking timepiece, and it's no wonder we feel distress!

For some of us, the theology is the hardest part to reconcile. We've had the path to exaltation laid out for us enough times to see with glaring clarity the step we seem to be missing. I've heard several intelligent, very spiritually oriented women comment on this fact and bemoan the perceived injustice. These women, who would happily partake of marriage should the right opportunity come along, express a sentiment something along the lines of "It doesn't seem fair or right that my progress toward exaltation is stopped because no one thinks I'm [fill the blank] enough to marry." They feel stuck and more than a little stagnant. But is it true? Are we singles lost to ourselves? With our unconventional status of undetermined duration, is this lifetime—a period meant to be used for great spiritual progress and growth—really a bust?

As believers in the "more excellent hope"[3] of the restored gospel of Jesus Christ, most of the women I know would see the falsehood of that idea. But the discontent in their situation remains. I've seen reactions to life as a single

2. For more inclusive approaches, see Sheri L. Dew, "Are We Not All Mothers?" and Dieter F. Uchtdorf, "Forget Me Not," *Ensign*, Nov. 2001, Nov. 2011; online at Magazines, *Church of Jesus Christ of Latter-day Saints*, www.lds.org/ensign/.

3. Ether 12:32.

woman that run the gamut from utter despair to gently simmering grief, from raw anger to grim acceptance, from constant anxiety to the low rumble of restlessness. True joy, I've noticed, is not often a part of the equation.

My dear friends, we can do better! It's my conviction that no matter where we stand in the gospel lineup, we have not only a perfect right to but a genuine responsibility for two things: our own joy and our own spiritual progression. And I'm not just referring to this in a time to come. I truly believe that no matter one's marital status, life—*this* life—can and should be intensely joyful and evolutionary spiritually.

"That They Might Have Joy"

Some readers may question my emphasis on happiness. I mention it because I've seen it promised so often in our liturgy, usually as an immediate promise rather than a distant, otherworldly one.[4] Joy becomes our inheritance the moment we embark on the path of salvation, as does our claim to spiritual growth. In the Book of Mormon, King Benjamin said it beautifully:

If ye have known of [God's] goodness and have tasted of

---

4. 2 Ne. 2:25; cf. Joseph Smith to Nancy Rigdon ("Happiness is the object and design of our existence and will be the end thereof if we pursue the path that leads to it"), LDS Church History Library, online at "Digital Collections," MS 155: Joseph Smith Collection, 1827–1844, Correspondence, 1829–1844, Letters sent, 1842, history. lds.org/section/library.

his love, and have received a remission of your sins, which causeth such exceedingly great joy in your souls, even so I would that ye should remember and always retain in remembrance, the greatness of God[,] and ... if ye do [these things] ye shall *always rejoice* and be filled with the love of God, and always retain a remission of your sins; *and* ye shall *grow in the knowledge of the glory of him who created you*, or in the knowledge of that which is just and true.[5]

I take this passage to mean I have permission to be joyful. All of us have permission, no matter what our age, occupation, marital status, or anything else.

When this idea became clear to me, I was so tired of discontent that I was ready to let it go. It struck me that there was no panic in heavenly realms when I reached particular milestones without an impending proposal of marriage. Any consternation about that was all mine. If I really believed that God does have "all wisdom and power, both in heaven and in earth," and we do "not comprehend all the things which the Lord can comprehend," then I needed to own up to my rights and blessings for happiness.[6] To do otherwise would be to choose a secondary gift.

I wonder if, as singles, we get so thick into the mindset of putting things on hold that we apply a deferment to our rejoicing as well. Or perhaps something in us feels

---

5. Mosiah 4:11–12, emphasis added.

6. Mosiah 4:9; cf. 1 Cor. 2:9.

compelled to be unhappy because our situation seems so linked to a doctrine of necessity. Yet the restored gospel is rife with precedents that address and resolve the problem of the unaccomplished necessity.[7] We singles have adequate proof that *every* blessing pertaining to the path of exaltation will be ours if we are faithful, whether in this life or the next.[8] With such clear and irrefutable promises about my present and my future, I have found that living with joy, coupled with very flexible hope, works wonderfully.

The Principle of Improvement

Keeping things in perspective has also proven useful when contemplating my single life. Culture and biology aside, what is it we want to accomplish in this life? Brigham Young put it this way: "What are we here for? To learn to enjoy more and to increase in knowledge and in experience."[9] Last time I checked, no relationship status had a monopoly on knowledge or experience.

I should add here that knowledge and experience do not always have to come through adversity, although it

---

7. The Nephites relied on the promise of Christ's future atonement (Jarom 1:11), and in the modern age we perform proxy ordinances in the temples (D&C 137:7–9). Thanks to Charisse Baxter for this insight.

8. "If in this life only we have hope in Christ, we are of all [women] most miserable" (1 Cor. 15:19).

9. John A. Widtsoe, ed., *Discourses of Brigham Young: Second President of the Church of Jesus Christ of Latter-day Saints* (Salt Lake City: Bookcraft, 1998), 87.

is the context we usually hear about in Sunday School. When actively and creatively sought, gaining knowledge and experience can be rewarding and enjoyable. Actually, knowledge and experience come to us whether or not we seek them. In the preoccupation of meeting all our life-expectations, we may not notice the new or reaffirming lessons of each moment. Yet, as a venerated Eastern philosophical tradition suggests, "All actions, without exception, culminate in knowledge."[10] I defer again to Brigham Young, whose pragmatism often brought clarity to obscure concepts:

> The first great principle that ought to occupy the attention of mankind, that should be understood by the child and the adult, and which is the mainspring of all action, whether people understand it or not, is *the principle of improvement*. The principle of increase, of exaltation, of adding to what we already possess, is *the grand moving principle and cause* of the actions of the children of men. No matter what their pursuits are, in what nation they were born, with what people they have been associated, what religion they profess, or what politics they hold, this is the mainspring of the actions of the people embracing all the powers necessary to perform the duties of life.[11]

I find his viewpoint to be profound. Whether or not we are conscious of it, he tells us, God is intimately at

---

10. Bhagavad Gita 4:32, trans. Deepak Chopra, *Sacred Verses, Healing Sounds: The Bhagavad Gita Audiobook* (San Francisco: Amber-Allen, 2004).

11. Widtsoe, *Discourses of Brigham Young*, 87, emphasis added.

work in our lives. A "grand moving principle" is launching each one of us toward improvement. Joseph Smith similarly noted that while troubling things occur in our lives, "God in the last days ... is not trifling with you or me."[12] This idea has become extremely comforting to me. I have found that as I actively look for and cooperate with this moving power in my life, that's when things get exciting!

To Bring to Pass Much Righteousness

As truly important as marriage and family are, I wonder how much of a disservice we single women do ourselves by unconsciously tying so much of our spiritual progress to a decision we can only half make. When we do so, we give away our power in a very real sense. I don't use that word in an egotistic or self-aggrandizing way, but rather in the sense of the "power that is in [us], wherein [we] are agents unto ourselves" to do "many things of our own free will and to bring to pass much righteousness."[13] When we wrongly assume that power to progress is granted only to the married, we stunt our own spiritual growth—growth that, in fact, is every bit as available to us as to our married counterparts.

True, there are godly things that married people learn that are less available to singles, but when I listen

---

12. Joseph Smith, *The Essential Joseph Smith* (Salt Lake City: Signature Books, 1995), 236.

13. D&C 58:27–28.

to my married friends talk about their most important lessons from marriage, they usually speak of patience, selflessness, cooperation, and unconditional love—traits we can all learn. Perhaps the difference is that, as singles, we do not have the requirement to develop these attributes thrust upon us. Our situation requires a more proactive approach. This is, in some ways, lucky for us. We are given the option to *choose* to learn some of life's lessons, with pronounced purpose rather than as an imposed necessity, through things married friends often describe in terms of trials.

Could we single women of the church consider our unconventional status as a divine compliment? Could we perceive it in a happy way: that for this particular section of our eternal path, God has trusted us to be resourceful, finding creative ways to grow in godliness? This is not at all meant to suggest that only we can be proactive spiritual learners. The choice of active versus passive participation in spiritual progress is universally available. But as a great believer in the power of women, I am convinced we were never expected to wait for any kind of permission to grow spiritually.

I say this because I've seen the growth I've sustained through this process in my own life. God is so clearly behind it. As I've begun to release my will to the greater Divine will, the beauty and glory of the path have become more apparent to me. As I have begun to give up my resistance, my path has filled with light, peace, and interestingly, love. I think that is a truth of godliness necessary in all aspects of life, married or single.

In the end, regardless of our status, we are all on this "grand moving" path together. We are children of God with infinite potential to do good and to become better. Our existence was designed for joy and for improvement. We owe it to our God, "who [preserves us] from day to day" and who "lends [us] breath, that [we] may live and move and do according to our own will" to do rich and radiant things with our lives.

I know a woman who was a major influence in my life. We were inseparable for years, she and I, until a soul-rending breakup terminated our relationship. Let's call her Giselle. That's a pretty name.

I can still picture her vividly: she had shiny hair, smooth skin, wide hips, and perfect breasts. She loved and cared for those around her. She was friendly and funny. Not that she was without her mistakes—nobody's perfect—but she immediately took appropriate steps to correct whatever she did wrong and maintain a clean slate with everyone, especially God.

Giselle kept a tidy home. She fought off the entropy of the universe—spitting in the face of the second law of thermodynamics, then polishing it till it shone—with her green-and-yellow scrub sponge and the might of her well-toned arms. She cooked, swept, and washed clothes and dishes and floors and windows as fervently as she pursued her daily scripture studies with her family and on her own. As a child I always felt welcome in her home, although it actually felt more like a temple than a home.

She was always appropriately and modestly dressed—not the kind of woman who would ever think of wearing flip-flops or pants to church. She often went on excursions with sister missionaries, bringing many people to the waters of baptism. She attended all three hours of church, all extra meetings related to her responsibilities as the Young Women's president, and of course all the ward talent shows and musical devotionals, as she was a naturally gifted musician.

Her daily prayers consisted of individual meditations, prayers with her husband, prayers with her family before school and before bedtime, and orisons over her nutritious meals, including snacks and less nutritious but equally prayer-worthy desserts. I've never known a woman who prayed as much or as fervently as Giselle did. And it seemed that all those prayers did the trick. Rarely did God fail to respond to her needs and wants, as far as I could discern. Even her desserts, once blessed, seemed to nourish and strengthen her body.

Last I saw her, she didn't seem to care that she was barred from holding the priesthood. She could receive all the priesthood blessings through the men in her life, and besides, her ability to summon spiritual aid through her own prayers and fasts seem to rival Elijah's purifying fire from heaven. I was admittedly jealous, as God had never answered my girl-aged prayers with such energy, no matter how long I remained on my knees or how many meals I skipped. I kept trying, though. Giselle inspired all those around her to do better and try harder, and she did so without ever seeming to be in a hurry, always available with an understanding ear. I felt that she must have had the power to manipulate the space–time continuum so she could complete her monthly visiting teaching assignments and grocery shopping and ironing (which I especially hated) and every other task that was hers. She even found time to make little scripture cards on high-quality recycled paper with raffia ribbons when it was her turn to teach at church.

This wonderful woman comforted and strengthened everyone she came in contact with. She reached out to people who had fallen away from church, warning me to "not get too close to those with dissenting views," only enough to convince them to return to religious activity. She took brownies to the bishop's family, cooked meals for new mothers, and cut flowers from her garden for people in the hospital. Her energy, transubstantiated, filled these lucky souls with substance and light. It was a Good Samaritan's application of Einstein's energy–mass transference. She was impervious to the wiles of the devil, although she once confessed to me that she had cheated on her diet and eaten chocolate (90 percent cacao, of course). But she would never cheat on her monthly fast, she said, and sometimes she fasted from lunchtime on Saturday to dinner on Sunday—instead of simply missing breakfast—to be sure she had given her all.

Her jewelry was nice but not overdone (one piercing per ear, as the church counseled), her clothes showed off her curves but not her skin or her temple garments. She saw her womanhood as synonymous with her wifehood and motherhood, which formed, I could tell, the core of her identity. She said she and her husband had empowering and satisfying sex, but when I bravely asked her one day what an orgasm felt like, she looked at me blankly and changed the subject. Once a week she and her husband went on a romantic date, sometimes to the temple. They spent Saturdays doing family research or adding to their food storage. To rotate the emergency food, Giselle slyly slipped whole wheat flour, pinto beans, and dehydrated milk into their daily meals. Her husband didn't even notice, her meals were that good. The pedestal he placed her on was so elevated he could not see any faults besides her insignificant personality quirks, which he found endearing. He admitted to other men that she was the reason he kept to the straight and narrow. I hoped one day my husband would value me as much as Giselle's husband obviously prized her.

In my twenties, I admired the couple's persistent good nature and motivation to improve themselves. Children would be the natural result of their love for one another and their willingness to obey God's command to multiply and replenish the earth. When she did become pregnant, Giselle switched from Zumba to a prenatal yoga class. Her only complaint the entire time was that she wished she could still fast while pregnant.

"Think of all those lost blessings!" she said sadly.

The way she described childbirth, there were angels and rainbows in the hospital room with her. I thought to myself that if having children was that wonderful, maybe I should want children too. At no time was she happier, she said, than when she was surrounded by her own little unit of heaven, a husband and 3+ children.

Her understanding of her eternal family did not include the presence of sister wives, I one day discovered, even though church leaders still hinted that plural marriage was the order of heaven. In fact, past church leaders had unequivocally stated that monogamy was wicked.[1] One time, in a weak moment of troubled honesty, Giselle admitted that she felt uncomfortable about the tone and content of Doctrine and Covenants 132—but, she hastened to add, seeing the look of agreement on my face, there was no need to worry, since God would sort everything out and it would all be fine. By the time

---

1. Apostle John Taylor suggested that "the one-wife system not only degenerates the human family, both physically and intellectually, but it is entirely incompatible with philosophical notions of immortality; it is a lure to temptation, and has always proved a curse to a people" (*Millennial Star*, Apr. 9, 1853, 227).

she reached heaven, she told me, her voice trembling with faith and fear, she would have progressed enough to be able to share her husband unselfishly with other women. And anyway, she had so many current concerns, there was no time to speculate about the next life or doubt the statements of church leaders.

Even Giselle's wholesome recreational activities were full of busyness and godliness, two traits that became synonymous in my mind. She organized family reunions and vacations, full of cherished memories, which were promptly recorded in her journal and in elegantly crafted scrapbooks. She didn't spend much time on the Internet, but when she did, her postings were sweet and encouraging. I imagined her typing distractedly on her computer while basking in the warmth of the family's hearth, one of those eco-friendly fireplaces. When she signed off, it was probably because she needed to breastfeed her babies and rock them to sleep. She liked to wake up early, just like Jesus and all the great prophets. And bakers and toilet cleaners, I grumbled to myself, but I felt ashamed because she also baked bread and cleaned toilets with skill and grace.

This faith-driven woman drove her children to various extracurricular activities and play dates, of course arriving on time and without resorting to road rage. Her children were adorable and smart and made in her image. She was on the PTA board and helped with fund-raisers at the school. She understood that her sacrifices in this life meant greater joy in the next. She had a personal relationship with Jesus, so personal that she wept whenever she mentioned His greater sacrifice for all humankind. It was because of Him, she testified, that she was able to live an ideal life and be happy and content as she helped build up the kingdom of God.

Who was this remarkable woman?

She was my God. A false one.

An Idolater's Confession

Giselle is not a real human being, as you might have guessed. She was a real enough presence in my life, however, a cruel, psychological taskmaster. She was a constant reminder of the attributes and activities needed to receive the love of God, the approval of my church leaders, and a place in heaven with my family. I could not argue with her obviously admirable qualities, so I became her obedient, if sometimes reluctant, slave.

She was not like the false gods of wealth ("gods of silver, and gold, of brass, iron, wood, and stone, which see not, nor hear, nor know," Dan. 5:23) or of war, as decried by President Spencer W. Kimball in his famous sermon, "The False Gods We Worship."[2] She did not represent anything in the material world; rather, she was a platonic ideal

---

2. Kimball, "The False Gods We Worship," *Ensign*, June 1976, online at www.lds.org/ensign/.

derived from good but ultimately unbalanced sources. My subconscious construction of her reminded me of the statue in King Nebuchadnezzar's dream, divided into segments.[3] For me, Giselle's golden head was formed from ideas I had gleaned from scriptures portraying women as prized for their beauty and described like precious metals, jewels, and property.[4] Her chest and arms were, in my imagination, similarly bejeweled with Western expectations of youth, health, and eye-catching adornment.

Most important of all was her womb, which was cast in bronze and reinforced by two centuries of Mormon culture—a culture that considered birth not only a commandment but also part of a woman's prerequisite for salvation (but hey, no pressure).[5] To this day, those who cannot have or do not want children are often pitied and treated as incomplete and immature.

---

3. Dan. 2:31–33.

4. See, e.g., Exod. 20:17; Prov. 31:10; 1 Cor. 11:8–9; 3 Ne. 3:13; D&C 132:62; Moses 4:22.

5. From church president Joseph F. Smith: "Motherhood lies at the foundation of happiness in the home, and of prosperity in the nation. God has laid upon men and women very sacred obligations with respect to motherhood, and they are obligations that cannot be disregarded without invoking divine displeasure. ... Can [a woman] be saved without child-bearing? She indeed takes an awful risk if she willfully disregards what is a pronounced requirement of God" (*Gospel Doctrine: Selections from the Sermons and Writings of Joseph F. Smith* [Salt Lake City: LDS Church, 1919], 288–89; qtd. in "Birth Control," *Eternal Marriage Student Manual*, 2003, online at www.lds.org/manual/eternal-marriage-student-manual/birth-control).

Giselle's iron legs had helped her endure the grueling walk across the prairies and had steadfastly bolstered her against an increasingly wicked world. She was able to walk in paths of righteousness without questioning where the path was taking her. I imagined her feet to be perfectly pedicured: dainty and soft from the clay-pack treatments they received and decorated with iron toe-rings, shaped from the perceptions and opinions of hundreds of trusted Mormons in my life, perceptions that were well formed and well defended but ultimately too fragile to ground my beliefs on.

For the most part, the gradual construction of this ideal woman took place each Sunday. As a little girl wearing a pretty dress and sitting on a hard beige chair, I paid close attention at church. I was surrounded by others my age who were similarly eager to be good. As I was one of those overachiever types, I was constantly confused at the injunction to obey all of the commandments but to avoid Pharisaic overzealousness. I was commanded to be perfect but told that Christ would make up for my failures. However, since every misdeed of mine created additional agony for the Savior, I determined that it was best not to make mistakes in the first place. I even wondered at one point how many drops of blood were literally spilled because of me, even though my list of childish peccadillos was short. Christ's suffering brought me no joy, only increased anxiety.

Giselle, in contrast, was so full of grace for others that she needed none herself. The ideals that formed her over the years—with each new good idea from the pulpit interpreted as a new commandment—were unattainable on a daily basis. There was not time enough in the day to accomplish all of them and maintain my sense of individuality.

Still, I watched other women in church to figure out who the right kind of woman was. Sister So-and-So was praised from the pulpit for the way she dedicated her life to the church, giving up any potential career or personal hobbies. Here was a woman of God, they said. On the other hand, Sister Such-and-Such was confident and had strong opinions that were met with an awkward silence, clearly indicating that she, despite her assertive spirit and success in her career, was not intended to be anyone's role model.

I began to struggle with the lessons presented to us in Young Women classes, where we were encouraged to see ourselves as princesses needing to be swept off our feet and carried to castle-like temples by priesthood-holding princes. We were to prepare now for our destiny as wives and mothers. Careers were fallback plans in case our prince never showed up or fell off his horse. My spirit chafed as I heard about the importance of temple marriage, modesty, children, and taking care of the home—Giselle's eternal kingdom—lesson after lesson. Physics and black holes were at least as interesting as boys and babies, I muttered to myself. Could I not be a scientist and a wife and mother? The question was met with a foreboding silence from heaven. President David O. McKay's 1968 slogan haunted my dreams of becoming an astrophysicist: *No other success can compensate for failure in the home.* I decided to keep up my studies in case I could find a way to do both without jeopardizing my eternal family.

I trusted the adults who told me I must do *x*, *y*, and *z* to maximize my happiness. Who would not want to be happy? I had to commit. Thus the immaterial ideal, Giselle, descended into the material real, my God incarnate, in framed pictures of the temple, gold necklaces stamped with the image of a perfect young woman, copies of "The Family: A Proclamation to the World," scripture handouts with raffia bows, Young Woman bookmarks and fake jewels and cross-stitched designs, and letters written to my future self asking how many children I had and what color my future husband's eyes were.

All these and more I collected as material offerings to my idol. My mother truly enjoyed staying at home and raising five children, aided by her genuine and laudatory talents in cooking, gardening, sewing, and professional cake decorating. I could also be a crafty stay-at-home mother if I had to be, I thought, although my heart wasn't in it. My mistake was to assume that every woman was *required* to like making crafts and to stay at home with her children to be truly righteous. I credit Mom's independent spirit and interest in education for creating a small wedge between Giselle and me. My mother encouraged my academic interests. She took me to the library, enrolled me in science camps, and generously praised my success in computer-programming, math, and physics contests. My father was immensely supportive as well. I was free to explore my academic desires by taking advanced high school courses in physics and calculus and working three summers at a cosmic-ray research facility at the University of Utah.

I enrolled as a freshman at Brigham Young University in 2002, a place of promised princes and carefully moderated education. Emboldened by my experiences to that point, I signed up for the astrophysics program. In the back of my head, I wondered if physics was too worldly a venture and might jeopardize my potential for marriage and raising children. Again I heard that haunting slogan, *No other success can compensate for failure in the home.* I heard it as I entered the Wilkinson Center to attend an orientation meeting for freshmen interested in astrophysics. Climbing the stairs to the third floor and finding room 3224, I stood anxiously at the threshold of the doorway and noticed how few women were there. Giselle was tugging at my arm, pulling me back into the hallway, begging me to consider my unborn children and the color of my future husband's eyes.

While Giselle was imaginary, the fear was real. I turned around and walked away before the orientation started. My future family took precedence over career aspirations, I told myself. In the heat of the moment, I forgot to remind myself that Jesus had said next to nothing about family and nothing at all about needing to stay at home. I overlooked the fact that men have it both ways: family life and a career too. I eventually chose an English major. I now regret that I made such a life-altering decision based on fear.

As I progressed through BYU, Giselle evolved into a sort of corrupt, freaky female replacement of Jesus, a resplendent female martyr and Stepford wife. Her highest pleasure was to seek salvation for herself and her neighbors, which meant getting and keeping everyone in line with church teachings. Jesus's injunction to "love thy neighbor as thyself" (Matt. 22:39), with its implication of self-regard rather than masochistic self-sacrifice, was lost somewhere among her good works. To be selfish—that is, to spend time on personal activities that did not somehow bless the lives of others—was akin to blasphemy.

Giselle even came to exceed Jesus in her authority and salvific might. I believed she had the power to spiritually save others, including anyone within testifying range. She was the "savior on Mount Zion" that Joseph Smith and my patriarchal blessing had mentioned.[6] As I

6. See, for instance, "Becoming Saviors on Mount Zion," ch. 41

now understand it, Christianity involves a commitment to love God and other people, to learn from our mistakes—not to save people from their sins by enrolling them in heaven. That kind of control over an individual's agency sounds like well-intentioned meddling to me.

At the time, I believed it was my responsibility to save other people. I served a Spanish-speaking mission in Toronto and daily pushed myself to approach perfect strangers and tell them what was wrong with their beliefs. Sitting primly on a low couch in a small apartment, smoothing out a wrinkle in my calf-length dress, I told a Mexican immigrant she should not wear such revealing clothes to church. Her face darkened and grew unreadable; she stopped coming to church. I found out that the woman felt insulted and thought I was trying to control her (I was). I had cared more about the height of her neckline than the depth of our friendship. I had sacrificed a real human connection on the altar of conformity.

Why couldn't I be like Giselle, I wondered, who won people over with her goodness? Her prayers for others called down the "tentacles of Divine Providence," as apostle Orson F. Whitney penned in 1929. The phrase still calls to mind a giant black octopus dragging people screaming to heaven. (Who needs the priesthood

in the Relief Society manual, *Teachings of Presidents of the Church: Joseph Smith* (Salt Lake City: LDS Church, 2007), 469–78.

when you've got divine tentacles?) I kept asking myself what Giselle would do—WWGD—since her schedule was always full of commendable plans. In her sweet, passive-aggressive way, she used anxiety, shame, and fear to keep me on her straight and narrow path: the road of religious scrupulosity. I remember doing good deeds purely out of pressure—because if I didn't, Giselle would make me pay emotionally, and she exacted more than a tenth. Jesus of the New Testament was nothing next to her Old Testament demands. In the twenty and second year of the reign of Giselle, however, something in me broke.

Breaking Down the Idol

The king's statue in the Bible was destroyed by a stone said to have been "cut without hands" (Dan. 2:34). I always pictured this stone as a massive granite boulder rolling down a jagged mountain. It wasn't until my mission that I felt like a stone had broken away and started rolling down the slopes of my soul. In the course of a bus ride through Toronto, one of the most international cities in the world, I found myself talking to people from Albania, Afghanistan, China, Ghana, Guatemala, India, and the Ukraine. There were certainly a lot of people who needed to be saved, I thought. After the homogeneity of Utah, I was startled to discover that not only did people have beliefs that differed so drastically from mine but they seemed content, even happy, with those beliefs.

Nevertheless, I reasoned that their apparent contentment couldn't be true happiness like mine, although I was often unhappy. Their disagreement, and sometimes abuse, strengthened my feeling that I was right and they were wrong.

Then in October 2006, some missionaries and I were in a meeting with our mission president when some elders called in asking if they could see the Broadway musical *Wicked*, which had come to town. "What will people say if they hear that I let my missionaries see a play called *Wicked*?" my mission president asked, laughing. But after a while he assented, especially after hearing that it was a retelling of *The Wizard of Oz* and was family friendly. We received permission too, so a few weeks later I was sitting in my missionary attire next to four other sister missionaries, all of us enveloped in a wave of green stage light as the tale we knew from childhood was turned on its head. In the Broadway version, the Wicked Witch of the West was portrayed as someone who had been misunderstood, and it made me wonder how many times I had seen wickedness in someone where there was none, where the frame of reference was so different as to render human judgment obsolete. Giselle, high on her pedestal, shifted uncomfortably but remained characteristically conflict-avoidant.

The rock began to gather momentum (let's call it the rock of awareness) as I finished my mission and faced my impending marriage to Andrew, whom I had dated during our time at BYU and who had corresponded with me throughout my mission. Before the big day, I sat down with Andrew—whose eyes were green, in answer to the teenage letter to myself—and for fun we filled out a Catholic marriage questionnaire a neighbor had given me. I discovered that my fiancé lacked Giselle's testimony of gender roles. I had assumed he would handle all the finances and I would do the housecleaning and child-raising, but in what was a radical and welcome change for me, we decided to share the financial responsibilities evenly. He also volunteered to wash the dishes if I would cook, since he hated cooking. I would be in charge of laundry (not ironing), while he would clean the bathrooms, which I hated doing. What a relief to know we would share the housework!

Later, when our son was born and we shared diaper changing and other baby responsibilities, I had to relinquish Giselle's obsessive-compulsive perfectionism to allow for Andrew's ideas of how to clean and take care of Max in ways he felt were best. Our arrangement served us well, and we divvied up other responsibilities as we went along. The instrument of Giselle's impending destruction gained even more force when we moved to Italy and I met a young Austrian named Sebastian. He and my husband were attending college together while I edited documents for an online business. One day during choir practice, where Sebastian and I were both tenors in the University of Bologna choir, I made a joke about homosexuals.

"You know I'm gay, don't you?" he said, kindly but directly. I sputtered, colored, and apologized. Being friends with him was like being forced to stare directly at a list of my previous prejudices, but I soon discovered that I could add one more brother to my growing family of friends.

In 2009 when we moved to Brussels for a summer internship, I noticed that there were plenty of women in the local ward who wore pants to church. Members were glad the women were there at all and no one mentioned their fashion choices. Since I had always hated wearing dresses, I began wondering what the official rules were; I had always assumed the church had a rule against women wearing pants on Sunday. I remembered on my mission having seen a solid, long-time member wear dress slacks to a sacrament meeting and thinking it was irreverent. One Sunday afternoon Andrew and I searched online for every LDS reference we could find on appropriate church attire and found only one explicit guideline saying the church had no objection to women wearing pants. The specific wording was that there was no restriction on "just how long women's or girls' dresses should be nor whether they should wear pant suits or other types of clothing." Summing up, the authorities explained that they had "not ... felt it wise or necessary to give instructions on this subject relative to attendance at our Church meetings."[7]

Yet in December 2013, four decades after this guideline had been given, women who wanted to bring awareness to cultural prejudices organized a Wear Pants to Church event and received threats from church members, including one death threat.[8] When women receive death threats for wearing pants to church, we obviously have a deep-seated problem we need to talk about as a culture. An online commenter asked, "What next? Men wearing dresses to church?" All I could think of was yes, the *dhoti* and *lungi* in India, the *kilt* in Scotland, the *foustanella* in Greece, the *gho* in Bhutan, the *pareo, lava-lava,* and *sarong* in the Pacific Islands and South Asia, the *kanga, kitenge, kikoy,* and *lappa* in sub-Saharan Africa, and the *caftan* and *djellaba* in the Middle East and North Africa. If my mission in Toronto had taught me anything, it was that people were different, and the majority of those differences were not evil. I started wearing dress pants to church, for which I received a few disapproving looks from older folks and had my temple worthiness

7. *Priesthood Bulletin*, June 1971, qtd. in Hortense H. Child, "When and Where Is It Acceptable for Young Women to Wear Pants When Involved in Church-Related Activities?" *New Era*, Dec. 1974, online at www.lds.org/new-era/.

8. Timothy Pratt, "Mormon Women Set Out to Take a Stand, in Pants," *New York Times*, Dec. 19, 2012. This despite the fact that the church confirmed its earlier 1971 announcement that women could wear what they wanted to church.

questioned by a counselor in the stake presidency. To his credit, once I explained there was no rule, he apologized and we parted on good terms. I kept going to church in pants and stopped worrying about what other members thought of me.

I became pregnant at the age of twenty-six. It was a leap of faith to decide to have a child, not knowing if I could be the kind of mother Giselle wanted me to be. Despite my prenatal yoga, baby books, classes, and other preparations, the birth was much worse than I had expected. My baby was an enormous 10.6-pounder. There were no angels. There were no rainbows. I lay in shock, the pain intensified by the subsequent agonies of breast-feeding and postpartum depression. A nurse told me the second child would be easier, and I openly wept at the thought. This was not my heaven.

Later that year, as I recovered, a conservative young couple in our ward recommended the book *Women Who Make the World Worse* by Kate O'Beirne. To be polite, Andrew began reading it and found that the author criticized Simone de Beauvoir, whom neither of us had heard of, for having led women away from their true nature. Intrigued by the scornful denunci-ations, Andrew read de Beauvoir's *The Second Sex* and realized how often he had assumed women were be-ings whose power and authority were less than men's. One Saturday as we drove to the countryside to pick strawberries, we started to talk about what men expect of women and why. It made me realize that from the time I was young, I had been told that femininity was in danger, just as de Beauvoir had described in her book. I had been exhorted to be a real woman, to remain a real woman as I grew older. It would appear that it was not sufficient for a woman to be female; to be considered a woman, she had to share in a mysterious and threatened reality known as femininity. Was femininity produced by the ovaries or was it a platonic essence? Could the donning of a rustling petticoat transform a female into this endangered creature?[9]

It would be years before I realized that de Beauvoir was challenging my Giselle and lending momentum to my rock of awareness. When we flew to the Marshall Islands, Andrew's first diplomatic post in the Foreign Service, and when we felt the blast of tropical humidity as the plane's door opened (Majuro Atoll is only seven degrees north of the equator), I noticed that many of the women who had decided to wear makeup had it dripping down their faces. I made a mental note to stop wearing it altogether, not that I had ever liked it anyway. Why had I worn it? Giselle had told me to.

In the absence of makeup and fashion, I began to wonder about different cultures elsewhere in the world

---

9. See de Beauvoir, *The Second Sex* (New York: Knopf, 1989), xix.

and throughout history. I discovered, working through our spotty Internet connection, that during the Renaissance white teeth were considered unattractive, that high heels were *de rigueur* for French men in the sixteenth century, that pink was for boys and blue for girls until about the 1920s in the United States, and that Marshallese women make fun of you if you shave armpits and legs. In our contemporary Western culture, where youth is idolized, women take pains to maintain what people in other cultures recognize as childish features, such as soft cheeks, a short chin, an upturned nose, and large eyes. The point of mascara, for example, is to accentuate the doe-like illusion of a child's eyes. When our time was done and we moved to Montreal, it was difficult for me to re-enter a world where women felt they had to pluck, starve, paint, pad, and Photoshop themselves.

The final blow for Giselle took place after I read historian Todd Compton's account of Mormonism's first polygamous family. I ordered his book, *In Sacred Loneliness: The Plural Wives of Joseph Smith*, for Andrew's birthday since he enjoyed reading about church history. Compton's book had received a Mormon History Association award; it has since been cited on the church's website as a legitimate source of Mormon history. This history, however, is the side of the story not told in Sunday school. The accounts came from primary sources in the women's own voices. The author relates the women's stories in dry-eyed fashion, but I was appalled. Some of the plural wives begged to be divorced so they could find someone who would actually love them and at least live with them. Leaders said that if women rejected their offers of plural marriage, they would be damned, which seemed more than a little manipulative to me. Since when was saying no to a marriage proposal grounds for damnation? Other sad and strange things were done in the name of God during this time. Wives were often kept in the dark while their husbands married other men's wives. Marriage was redefined to accommodate this adultery.

I recalled the unease I had felt on my mission when a woman, on the eve of her baptism, had asked in tears about plural marriage after seeing a special on TV. My companion and I had soothed her with rationalizations I now realized were not substantiated by history. I felt sick.

After re-reading section 132 of the Doctrine and Covenants together, Andrew and I concluded that plural marriage was a failed experiment that largely benefitted the men at the expense of women. I finally felt free to reject a doctrine that had always disturbed me, a doctrine in which women were "given" to men to reproduce (v. 63). I am not someone to be given away, I realized. I am an agent unto myself, with power and authority over my own body and my own future. Among other things, this meant Andrew and I could now truly live together as equal partners.

Somewhere deep in my soul, I felt a mighty quake, and the granite boulder leapt from the base of the mountain and struck Giselle's lofty pedestal. My ears rang with a deafening roar that no one else heard. When the dust settled, Giselle and her pedestal lay in ruins.

Seeking Better Models

I've often wondered if Giselle would have had as much power if my culture had allowed Heavenly Mother a stronger place in its day-to-day consciousness. Would it have been easier to reject subconscious and harmful idols if the divine feminine were more openly acknowledged? Mormons are unique in believing in heavenly parents; however, in acknowledging and simultaneously ignoring the female side of deity, the ladder of importance is protected and a message of silence and submission is handed down to women. David L. Paulsen, a BYU professor, assisted by Martin Pulido, researched statements from church authorities and found that there is no official statement concerning the need to maintain silence about Heavenly Mother. Forbidding the very mention of Her, as some leaders now do, is a recent cultural phenomenon.[10]

---

10. Paulsen and Pulido, "'A Mother There': A Survey of Historical Teachings about Mother in Heaven," *BYU Studies* 50, no. 1 (2011): 75. See also *Sunstone* magazine's March 2012 issue on motherhood and its complexities.

One of the paradoxes of Heavenly Mother is that while faithful women are expected to be the primary caregivers in raising children, Heavenly Mother is conspicuously absent. Members are warned not to pray to Her. When I was president of the Young Women in my ward, I tried to add Heavenly Mother to our theme to read, "We are daughters of our Heavenly Father and Heavenly Mother, who love us, and we love Them." My bishop and stake president told me to stop. It was a terrible and confusing experience to have to tell my class of young women we couldn't acknowledge our Heavenly Mother. True, Her existence has been confirmed by the male leaders, but She remains an empty placeholder in Mormon theology. Her absence in the Young Women theme and elsewhere speaks volumes to Mormon women all over the earth.

Without a worship-worthy Mother, we must find pieces of the divine feminine elsewhere, in other women. I admire Debbie, a Relief Society president in New York who is strong-willed and unapologetically herself. Her genuineness rubs off and makes me feel more at home in my own skin. I love that when she overheard a local leader say, "We put our women on a pedestal," she interrupted with, "I'm not a damn statue." I have been fortunate to know many women like Debbie whose gifts I appreciate. I don't feel the need to be exactly like them, but their real-time joys, frustrations, sorrows, successes, and failures are better models than any cosmically powerful ideal.

I don't blame anyone in particular for the subconscious role model I chose for so long to emulate. As human beings, we see patterns and archetypes around us, classifications based on observation we sometimes admire and adopt. This is how we make sense of the world, or try to. However, the models fall short of the complexity of life, which far surpasses a "men are from Mars and women are from Venus" mentality. When we accept that kind of superficiality, it causes real harm to real people here on earth. I suspect that other people have their own models of perfection, that Giselle has many relatives.

Jean Piaget, a Swiss cognitive theorist, suggested that as children mature, they construct and then refine psychological structures called schemes, which are mental representations of images or concepts of life experiences. These schemes—a ball is round, a car honks, a woman looks like x and does y—are adapted and linked with other schemes when new information challenges the old.[11] It is only when the schemes are challenged that we can become aware of, and begin to rethink, inaccurate or incomplete perceptions.

I like the challenge to a one-size-fits-all assumption in Nassim Nicholas Taleb's *The Black Swan: The Impact of the*

---

11. Laura E. Berk, *Child Development*, 7th ed. (Boston: Pearson, 2006), 221.

Highly Improbable, in which he explains that "categorizing is necessary for humans, but it becomes pathological when the category is seen as definitive, preventing people from considering the fuzziness of boundaries, let alone revising their categories."[12] And so, despite my respect for the position of a general authority, I disagree with LDS apostle Bruce R. McConkie's limited, now fifty-year-old definition of women in *Mormon Doctrine*, which even the publisher's note warned "should not be considered an official statement of doctrine" (but was only recently discontinued by the church-owned publisher):

> Setting the pattern for all her daughters in all ages, Eve's mortal mission included two special assignments: 1. She was to be an help meet for her husband (Moses 3:20); and 2. She was to bring forth children. "I will greatly multiply thy sorrow and thy conception," the Lord said. "In sorrow thou shalt bring forth children, and thy desire shall be to thy husband, and he shall rule over thee" (Moses 4:22). Thus woman's primary place is in the home, where she is to rear children and abide by the righteous counsel of her husband."[13]

In contrast, the definition of "man" in *Mormon Doctrine* was sweeping in its grandeur and perspective: "Man and God are of the same race, and it is within the power of

---

12. Taleb, *Black Swan* (New York: Random House, 2007), 15.

13. McConkie, *Mormon Doctrine*, 2nd ed. (Salt Lake City: Deseret Book, 1966), 844.

righteous man to become like his Father, that is to become a holy Man, a Man of Holiness."[14]

The first definition is proscriptive and the second expansive. Additionally, Elder McConkie's definitions cannot be universally applied. Even setting cultural differences aside, not everyone marries and not all women have or want children. Women don't all stay at home, even if they have the opportunity to do so. You can't have an equal partnership if there is a patriarchal chain of command where one is obligated to abide by the other's righteous counsel, but not vice versa. I applaud the remark of Cordelia Fine, a neuroscientist and mother, in her excellent *Delusions of Gender*: "It makes a difference what we believe about difference."[15] To expect all women to fit a narrow definition creates emotional havoc among our people.

As we free ourselves from idolatry, or what we may call idealatry—the worship of an ideal—we open our hearts to legitimate differences among us. In stating this I am conscious of the possibility of being misunderstood. I am not suggesting that we give up worthy goals and good deeds or even that we quit putting on makeup and aspiring to great hair. I am talking about the freedom from feeling beholden to an unrealistic cultural standard.

---

14. Ibid., 466.

15. Fine, *Delusions of Gender: How Our Minds, Society, and Neurosexism Create Difference*, Kindle edition (New York: Norton, 2010), 184.

The freedom from the pressure to perform and please others regardless of our personal needs and desires. The freedom to stop mimicking who we think we *ought* to be and start thinking about who we *want* to be.

These days I laugh more and judge less. I am less self-conscious. I am no longer hostage to a constricted definition of how I should experience joy. I am reading and writing about science again—as a wife and mother—and feel immense joy as I do so. I love being with my little family, but I do not feel the need to prove that love to anyone else to show how righteous I am. I am the author of my own slogans: *No success in the home can compensate for failure to listen to your own soul.*

The name Giselle comes from an Old Norse word, *gísl*, meaning *hostage*. I find this etymology applicable to me as a recovering idolater, since I was constrained by Giselle in many ways. Yet she was also hostage to me, as I was the one who assembled her in the first place, an Ozymandias built to honor my works and my greatness, an Ozymandias doomed to fail and fall.

Her presence is mostly gone from my mind now. A few bits of her are scattered here and there, but her pedestal remains broken. Her absence feels strange, like wind blowing across your head when you are used to wearing a hat. I do not miss her.

7 | Choosing Joy

Brooke Stoneman

"No more cookies in the cookie jar. No more money in the bank," my reproductive endocrinologist explained in his thick Lebanese accent. He provided several other analogies with equal gusto, and it would have been funny if the news wasn't devastating. After three years of trying to start our family, I was diagnosed with premature ovarian failure which, as my doctor so succinctly put it, means "no more eggs in the basket." People with premature ovarian failure do not have sufficient reproductive egg quality or quantity to conceive; for me, the probability of conceiving was slim, if any at all. To be diagnosed at twenty-seven is rare.

How do you process news like that? I left the clinic and trudged through snowy Washington, DC, streets to the metro in a state of shock. I made no attempt to retain my composure on the metro car as tears ran down my face. When I arrived and ascended to the upper platform, I found myself a stop too far. In the freezing cold, wearing my sweatpants and an old baseball cap, I stared up at the Arlington Cemetery sign from the platform. With my husband at work and family still asleep back home in Utah, a walk in the national cemetery seemed appropriate. In hindsight, I'll admit, it seems melodramatic. As I walked up and down the rows of tombstones bearing names and dates of death, I was overwhelmed with a sense of grief—even as I saw the degree to which my tragedy paled in comparison to theirs. The reality of such indiscriminate suffering in the world made me even more emotional.

Later I realized that my experience with infertility was creating a reservoir of compassion I previously lacked for the challenges inundating others. It also helped me gain a long-term perspective for my own life. It didn't mean that things weren't painful and confusing—they still are sometimes—but over the years my husband and I have come to a place of real joy. Joy in our marriage; joy in our life, our family, our individual accomplishments. But before choosing and working toward this joy, I found myself in a serious struggle to understand two things: my relationship with God, whose nature I was beginning to question, and my value as a woman.

Deity, Divinity, Disillusionment

When I was first diagnosed, I was hopeful. I had always been healthy. My husband had just been hired out of graduate school, and we had insurance to pursue treatment. But as weeks and months passed and pregnancy tests turned up negative, I began to despair. In a spiritual context, I grew up thinking about consequences: we're blessed for the good we do and ... well, not blessed for behaving poorly. Infertility is a pretty serious "not blessing," and at some point in my grieving process, I visited the idea that I had, in fact, done something to bring this on myself. *We did wait three years to try and have a baby. And I did single-date in high school even though my seminary teacher told me I shouldn't.* I told myself I didn't really believe these things caused my infertility, but on some level I wondered if the fire and brimstone of my Especially For Youth–inspired faith wasn't raining down on me for past sins. I understood God less like a merciful father and more like a sword-of-justice-swinging micromanager.

I turned to the scriptures, but to be honest, it didn't help. I was looking to the wrong patterns for insight. When Elizabeth couldn't have a baby, she prayed and became pregnant. Sarah couldn't have a baby, so she prayed and became pregnant. All I had to do was pass a test of faith and I would be cured. Isn't that what I was teaching my Primary kids?

I developed immense empathy during this time for gay and lesbian members of our church who have offered similar heartfelt prayers in anguish. Many men and women pray fervently for God to take away their feelings of same-gender attraction. They make deals with God based on personal righteousness, hard work, and determination, not unlike I had. Why don't those feelings go away? Because they don't want it enough? Didn't I want a baby enough? Aren't we as worthy of having our prayers answered as everyone else?

In my darkest moments, I questioned the very nature of God. Was He good? Did He care about us as individuals? Enough to intervene and make us whole, like in the New Testament? But mostly, my grief took the form of self-flagellation. Yes, God was good and He cared about us, but first we had to be worthy of the miracles we sought. I couldn't figure out which aspect of my relationship with Him I was neglecting. Surely there was something I could do that would square me with God and allow me to obtain the righteous desires of my heart.

Without Motherhood, What's Left?

A common side effect of infertility is feeling you are less of a woman because you cannot bear children. You shrink away from your husband, your girlfriends, your own body. I wonder sometimes if LDS women feel this more than others because of the church's family emphasis— that a woman's truest calling and most self-actualizing achievement in life is to bear and rear children, as we so frequently hear in church.

Our female role models in scripture are portrayed as valuable almost exclusively for their fertility. Even Mary is an example of that. We place her in high esteem because of her sacred calling to be a mother and the virtue and bravery that entailed. In other words, in the scriptures, there are very few women who, beyond a brief incident or statement, were beloved outside of their maternal role. The barren women among them, Elizabeth and Sarah, are portrayed as objects of pity until they receive a reward for their faithfulness, a child.

For a long time, it felt like every Relief Society lesson was titled "How Can I Teach [fill in the blank] to My Children?" or "How Can Motherhood Teach Me [blank]?" I admit, oversensitivity runs rampant when you cannot bear children, but these lessons made me wonder how I could ever hope to be a faithful LDS woman if I wasn't also a mother.

Moving Forward

For months I circled around the idea of what true womanhood was, waiting for something to change about our childless reality. When it became clear that we would not have biological children, I began taking a more active role in moving on. That's not a moment when you decide it doesn't matter; it's an ongoing series of choices about how you'll find meaning in your life despite loss.

At first I was paralyzed by how many options there were. Should we pursue more treatments or adopt? I could focus more on my career. We could devote more time to civic causes. But the most powerful question I started asking myself wasn't "What will I do?" but "What true principles will help me determine what to do?" It took some time to wade through the collection of false doctrines, personal doubts, and cultural add-ons I had accumulated over the years and allowed to define my experience.

To start with, I had to stop equating womanhood with motherhood. When church prophets have spoken about the divinity of women, they have always spoken of the eternal and innate qualities we are born with. Motherhood is important, but it is not the qualifying life event that ushers us into "real" womanhood. The experiences of the single sister, the childless wife, and the mother of many are equally valid: their spiritual strengths and value as women are independent of the rings on their fingers or the number of mouths at their dinner tables.

In recent years, conservative religious groups, including the LDS Church, have garnered negative attention for reinforcing demeaning and diminutive stereotypes about women. External criticism is one thing, but the real heartbreak is when the people inside these religious structures begin to confuse cultural, patriarchal conservatism with true doctrine. I'm not talking about women and the priesthood but about the way we perceive a woman's value, specifically that her value is tied up in the things that are "womanly" and "motherly." The

meaning of discipleship and womanhood itself is de-
valued when faithful womanhood is limited to baking,
bearing children, and cross-stitching instead of prac-
ticing charity, feasting on the scriptures, defending the
faith, and tending to the sick.

But coming to these conclusions about womanhood
wasn't enough. Another choice on my way to joy was to
stop obsessing about my value "as a woman" altogether.
I was otherwise the same person I had been before I
learned I could not have children. What about my en-
during value as a human being, a worker, a friend, an
artist, a life partner, a contributing member of my community? Certainly my identity isn't limited to my gender
and its reproductive abilities. I had to re-evaluate and
expand what my gender meant to me.

I also had to revisit the idea that not receiving re-
quested blessings meant a lack of personal righteousness.
God doesn't work that way. Not that He can't perform
miracles or that He doesn't answer prayers, but I had to
learn that our relationship with God isn't a vending ma-
chine where we deposit the right amount of righteous
coinage in exchange for the blessings we desire. He doesn't
love us less when we don't get what we want, and realities
of loss and sadness don't mean we are being punished.

In the Gospel of John, Jesus comes across a man
who had been blind since birth, and His disciples ask,
"Master, who did sin, this man or his parents, that he was

born blind?" Jesus answers, "Neither this man sinned nor his parents; but that the works of God should be made manifest in him."[1] Jesus seems to reject the premise that bad things in life always have a direct causal link to behavior. What matters is the Atonement, which gives us the ability to move past something and to make our hearts whole again.

Our Choices Define Us

When I wrote this essay, I knew I didn't want to say, "Boo-hoo, infertility is hard." I wanted to describe how infertility has caused me to reorient myself based on truer principles, to determine my future when so many options had been taken away. The moment I realized I had the ability to choose, in what seemed like a choiceless situation, came after returning from a second meeting with my reproductive endocrinologist. With a greasy Reuben sandwich in my hand, I plopped down on a barstool in the basement café of my apartment building, called my mother, and burst into tears.

"You know, Brooke, some people choose not to have kids, and that's okay too," she said.

That simple statement from my mother shook the earth for me. Even though it had been drilled into my head that choosing not to have kids was the height of

---

1. John 9:2–3.

selfishness, I could, in fact, choose not to have children and it wouldn't be evil. I had volition. I didn't have to pursue fertility treatments immediately so I could fit in with my friends at church. I didn't have to let guilt propel me to start the adoption process the next day to please God. I could stop being a victim and start dealing with the realities that life had given me.

When my husband and I moved to Morocco a few months later, I was still struggling with these issues, but two experiences galvanized my desire to make a new social and theological space for myself and my family instead of cowing to cultural pressure. While I was unpacking boxes in our new apartment, I came across an article written many years ago by Ardeth G. Kapp, who did not have children despite being president of the church-wide Young Women program. In her article, "Just the Two of Us—For Now," she told of a childless woman "who, at age fifty-eight, went into the hospital for a hysterectomy. The woman couldn't handle the emotional impact of that event, and she wept bitter tears of anguish, saying, 'Now I know that I'll never have any children.'"[2]

"Oh, absolutely not!" I said aloud. At twenty-seven, the idea of spending the rest of my life "in loneliness, waiting, never facing reality and never able to make the

2. Kapp, "Just the Two of Us—for Now," *Ensign*, Feb. 1989, online at www.lds.org/ensign/.

adjustments that could have brought [me] a full life,"[3] as Kapp put it, seemed horrible and unthinkable. But it was what I had been doing all along.

At that point, my husband and I stopped considering the "at all costs" fertility measures so many told us were necessary. We rejected treatments that put my health at risk. We put expensive treatments that would lead to financial ruin on hold until we could responsibly afford it. We quit basing our current joy on the presence of a future child in our lives. I stepped off the emotional roller coaster to consider what life would be like without children, and for the first time in months, I was really happy. I was happy to be free from the paralyzing standstill that was affecting my ability to be the kind of person I wanted to be.

I started seeing a doctor in Morocco to help manage the side effects of ovarian failure. However, as time went on, I realized he was treating me to get pregnant and not to ease the pain and discomfort associated with the condition. Every time we met he wanted to make sure I knew that I didn't have many birthing years left.

"You just need to know that things are really bad," he'd say.

"Yes, I know. I don't want to pursue any more treatments right now."

---

3. Ibid.

"I don't think you understand your situation. Why don't you want to have babies? Is it your marriage?"

"No, my marriage is fine, the best it's ever been, in fact. This is our choice."

My assertions baffled him every time. Over the last few years, I've had to re-align many assumptions about what a happy future looks like; some were assumptions others had for me, and some I had for myself. Speaking honestly, I still have occasional lapses where I am catapulted back into baby limbo. I feel pressure to put everything in my life on the backburner, "stay positive," and hang out until I am fifty-eight, just to make sure I have really exhausted my biological options. But I just can't live like that. The agency God has given us isn't just to choose right from wrong but to choose life from death, action from passivity, joy from belabored sorrow.

This isn't to say that decisions regarding our family are done being made, but that I am not going to wait for a miracle to start living a full and joyful life. No matter what happens, I feel more able to make that choice free from a false culture of maternal worship, misplaced identity, and religious guilt.

I'm not exactly grateful that I cannot bear children, but I cherish the knowledge and perspective I've gained through this process. Infertility, though difficult and frustrating, set me on a path of better understanding my innate human value and my relationship with God. I still feel that God is good, that He loves us, but this love does not mean He can always grant our material wishes. It does mean, however, that He can heal our hearts and make our lives meaningful. He gives us the "good part" described in Luke, which is the gospel, His Atonement, and joy.[4] And to receive that good part, we have to reject cultural myths and false religious tyranny that keep us from God and from our own lasting contentment. We have to choose joy, especially when it doesn't come easy.

---

4. Luke 10:42.

8 | Turquoise

Ashley Mae Hoiland

A woman in Tonopah, Nevada, gave me a raw chunk of turquoise on Sunday. She asked if I liked the light or dark, the green or blue, and then she dug through the rubble of plastery rocks in a plastic bag she had until she found the perfect piece, deep lake green with a rift of steamy blue. The shape: an upside-down house with inlets and points, a fracture near the bottom cracking out toward the regular gray specks in the back, covering it like a dusty mask.

My husband, son, and I could have found a Mormon chapel that morning as we traveled through the small town, but we didn't. We wound through the hot desert buildings downtown and talked across a glass case full of jewelry to a woman who told us about her family, and we told her about ours. We talked about work, about everyday-people things. She asked if I liked turquoise.

For most of my life, I've been eager for strangers to notice the small details that give away my Mormonness: the longer shorts, the curious light in a Mormon's countenance, my clean speech, my desire to be helpful in any situation. Lately though, I've found myself hoping people won't notice those things because I don't want to be asked questions I don't have answers for, particularly in regard to homosexuality and the church.

I believe homosexual marriage is valid, and that belief is not supported by LDS teachings. Currently, a homosexual person who is in a same-sex relationship or acts on romantic feelings with a member of the same gender is not qualified to hold church callings, take the sacrament (Eucharist), marry in the temple, or maintain membership in the church in many cases.

The issue is not one I've wondered about from afar. Like many church members, I've walked along with dear friends who have suffered in isolation, feeling guilt for what appears to be most natural to them, and I've watched many of them distance themselves, then separate from the church. I ache for those who feel unwelcome despite the attempts of people like myself to include them.

I felt a surprising sense of gladness to be interacting with someone in the turquoise-jewelry store as a person, rather than as a Mormon. There is liberation but also homesickness in taking a step back, if even for a day. In the past years, more than ever before, I've felt the pull to leave my religion at the same time I've felt a deeper longing to embrace the faith my whole life has been settled in. This past year, I've become acquainted with the incongruity between what I feel and what the church policies are. I want to be critically minded, yet I don't want to allow the sting of uncertainty to prick too deeply. I've learned that belief is a precious thing I don't want to lose. The turquoise piece the woman handed across the glass counter was half the size of a plum seed. It was the most opaque thing I have ever held, something that would be impossible to look through even if the brightest light were shining on the other side. Every unknown thing in the world could have burrowed itself inside that bottomless color.

I kept the turquoise in the glove box for the remainder of our week-long road trip. I pulled it out periodically: in Lee Vining, Mammoth Lakes, Yosemite National Park, and even in Modesto when it was too dark to see it. Every time I thought of the soft-armed woman in the middle the barren desert offering up such treasures to strangers. I thought of the rock that was now my treasure. I thought of the refining process the rock went through, the earth's millions of years of mineral records. I thought of how we are all similar to the opaqueness of the turquoise, that the pressure to create a thing of beauty and the weathering to give it personality is evident in ourselves. Creation of beauty, like the creation of anything valuable, is a process, and this process is synonymous with time, trial, work, and even heartache.

Our individual spiritual paths mimic the story of my tangible treasure. No doubt, as we navigate our life paths, the experience stretches, morphs, and marks our souls in a process that sometimes pulls us so deep inside the conglomeration of experiences we cannot see what is forming in the process. My own spiritual path may be different from that of other people, but it may be similar in the way it involves times of doubt and other times when there are bright reasons for hope and an armory of faith, an honest striving for Christlike charity.

On my desk near the front door, I have two small paintings showing a deer looking ahead and another similar deer turned to the side. I painted these for the new twin baby girls in my neighborhood, but the paintings became lost among piles of things I have to mail. The babies live ten houses away, but for the past month I haven't been able to gather the courage and go and offer the gift to their mothers, lesbians who got married and decided to adopt while one is in graduate school at Stanford. I haven't gone over because I don't know how I can answer their questions about me being Mormon. Maybe they won't care, but I will. I want to speak to them with the same ease I felt when talking to the woman in Tonopah. I want to interact with people without unanswered questions looming in the background. I don't want to be an ambassador, especially one who fumbles through her words and doesn't know how to defend the church's stance on gay marriage. I know I am not the only one who faces this spiritual crisis.

The Cantonese translation of the word *crisis* consists of two characters: *danger* and *opportunity*. I've thought about the application of that dual meaning in my current spiritual dilemma. I have learned to give new names to the crises I encounter in my life, actively looking for opportunities to turn them into moments of growth, empathy, maturity. For me, the church has always presented a context in which I can wrestle with hard questions. It offers me a place to work things through in my head and heart that I might not otherwise consider. It provides a reason for me to pray for and think about people. It encourages me to try to place myself in the minds of others. The church offers me a space where I can learn to be better. If most of us vacillate between blind faith and complete skepticism, I am still on the side of faith even if, at times, it is just 51 percent that tips the scale.

I cannot explain why my homosexual friends are disqualified from privileges I have as a married heterosexual woman. I hope things will change so that their marriages will be recognized. I want to go to my neighbors with my two paintings and offer them friendship and love without my religion's policies standing between us. Along with other Mormon women, I am trying to navigate a spiritual path as both a woman and a twenty-first-century human being, which is an incredible place to find myself. I am not complaining. I find there is room to think, act, and learn about an infinite number of topics within a context that isn't perfect but is full of people who cheer me on.

There are times when the weight of discrepancies seems like it will break everything my life has gathered to itself, but there are other countering moments of joy that make my heart burst like wildflowers being thrown into a warm breeze. There is also every moment in between: mostly simple and quiet moments rife with humanness. I live for and love the millions of moments in between, which are what the deep, inside color of the turquoise is made of. For me, a life of church membership and hope in the fundamental gospel truths that Christ taught are what make the gem's color vibrant.

I began to come to peace with my questions the night my husband and I sat at dinner with someone who says he has a hundred logical reasons why he should leave the LDS Church but hasn't. While my little son tottered around under the dinner table for over an hour after we had finished our giant bowls of soup, the man told us what he understood about the story of Job. He thought there was more to be gleaned from it than remaining faithful in the face of material loss. It is the story, he said, of a man whose understanding didn't match the views of his friends and his church. It's about a man who went to God in frustration. A man who even yelled at God, and God in turn "answered Job out of the whirlwind" to put him in his place, saying to Job, "Canst thou draw out leviathan with an hook?"[1] Even so, God loved Job for posing questions rather than simply stepping away. The questions were difficult and were expressed with anger, but God loved Job's honesty and blessed him for it.

This is how the man in our congregation defended his own questioning. From all appearances, you would think he was one of the stalwarts in the ward. He is the choir director and leads the vocalists with raw emotion. He is usually the only one to volunteer if a substitute is needed to teach a class of rowdy eight-year-olds. I love watching him conduct music with authentic joy or teach a lesson to children with enthusiastic inflection—knowing that he too has his fair share of questions.

In my own life, I don't want questions to cancel out my ability to find peace. I've learned that the things I doubt or do not understand are not indicative of a faltering character but are endemic to humans everywhere, and I can still move forward with joy even in the midst of them. A crisis can be an opening-up to things more beautiful and complex, so there is no need to put all aside and despair. My spiritual journey is full of more turns and surprises than I ever anticipated, and I suppose I may not understand why some things are the way they are for a long time.

That Sunday in Tonopah, the woman with a husband who works the mines sealed a lone bright rock in a

---

1. Job 38:1; 41:1, a leviathan being a large sea or land monster.

cellophane bag and accepted our sincere thanks but nothing more. Though that perfect piece of turquoise came from a rubble of ugly rocks, it is as smooth as the skin on the back of my little son's neck. The gift, the quick bits of thickest greens and blues, found its way to my palm like an omen, like a reminder that I am not alone. I know a God who listens to our questions and is not upset when we ask them. The turquoise reminds me of a stillness that happens when I stop everything and ask my Heavenly Parents if They love me. In the quietness of the many moments after, the answer is yes. And if They love me, I know They love all Their children. I hold tightly to that.

9 | I'll Go Where You Want Me to Go

Sylvia Lankford

> And he inviteth them all to come unto him and partake
> of his goodness; and he denieth none that come unto
> him, black and white, bond and free, male and female.
>
> —2 Nephi 26:33

I grew up in Alexandria, Virginia, eight miles from Washington, DC. My mother, father, sister, and I attended a Christian church as part of an all-black congregation. It was within walking distance, approximately two minutes from our home. My parents held leadership positions in the church, thereby setting an example for my sister and me. We were involved as ushers, sang in the choir, and participated in Sunday school.

In our home we read and studied the Bible and sought to gain a testimony of the Savior. Learning and knowing His word was important to me; I studied the scriptures and listened intently to the sermons I heard. The messages in the hymns and other songs were influential in my spiritual development. Later in life, I saw how my upbringing helped me seek further religious enlightenment.

My discovery of a fuller version of the gospel began when two young men knocked on the door. They wore badges identifying themselves as elders, my husband told me, since I was not home that evening. On hearing that the two young men had a message about Jesus Christ, he let them in and discovered what church they represented. The message they shared got my husband so excited he couldn't wait to tell me. He set up another time for them to come back so I could meet them as well.

The next time they visited, I was at home and listened intently to their message. They started answering questions I had carried in my heart for a long time. I had wondered if my husband and I could do more to help our children obtain a lasting testimony of the gospel message. Up to that point in time, I had felt there was something missing from my knowledge of Jesus Christ. With the missionaries teaching me, the missing pieces seemed to fall into place.

We invited the elders to come back again and again, and each week there was more to learn. We felt the Spirit grow stronger until they asked about baptism. This was a setback because I had already been baptized when I was about eleven years old, and I could not understand why I would need to be baptized again. The missionaries, Elders Campbell and Erickson, took the time I needed to have the ordinance explained to me as something that needed to be performed under the proper authority. Then I understood the centrality of baptism in this new faith.

It was amazing to learn about the fullness of the gospel and the beliefs of the LDS religion. As I learned more, other questions popped up. I had seen the missionaries and had met a few church members, most significantly the man who later became our first home teacher and a good friend, but I had not seen anyone of our race at church. I had the feeling the church was intensely good, according to what I had received thus far, but what about the members themselves? I wondered.

Other questions came to mind too: Would we make friends? Was it right for us to leave our previous church and venture into new territory? Would we have to worry about not being fully accepted because of the color of our skin? My husband raised these questions with the bishop, who assured us we would not have to worry. For us, this turned out to be true.

In an effort to show us more about the church, Elders Campbell and Erickson took us to the Washington Temple Visitors Center one evening, where we viewed the exhibits and talked with other missionaries. As the evening progressed, the elders took us to a side room and suggested that we pray, also that I should be the voice. What happened next was a defining moment for me. As

I got on my knees, I felt a heaviness come over me that weighed me down so I was unable to get the words out. I wanted to give thanks to my Father in Heaven for our blessings and to pray about what we had learned that evening, but instead this weight continued to prevent me from speaking.

I began to pray in my mind, asking Heavenly Father to help me speak and wondering why I was feeling this. What I decided was that Satan was trying to hold me back from learning anything further about the church. That realization made me think that if Satan would try so hard to stop me, then I must be doing something right; there must be something precious about the church. This thought piqued my interest enough that I struggled intently to finish my prayer, and after what seemed like an eternity, I felt the heaviness released and found I could complete my effort to speak. From that experience, I knew the LDS Church was the denomination I needed to join, notwithstanding our ethnicity. And despite what others may think of my spiritual experience at the visitors center, I was convinced the Lord had confirmed to me that the church was where He wanted me to go.

When some of my family members and friends heard that I was thinking of joining the church, they questioned my decision and advised me to look up information on the Internet. They even printed out unfavorable material for me to see. One of the articles they found gave a history of how blacks had not been able to hold offices in the church in times past. They asked me why I would leave my people and whether I would be accepted by the members of the LDS Church.

These questions disturbed me. I had not thought of this as an abandonment of my race. The way I looked at it, I was going where I needed to go to gain more insight into the gospel and to progress further in life. I knew who I was and where I came from, which was not something I could easily forget or give up. With the spiritual confirmation I received in the temple visitors center, a line from the well-known Baptist hymn came to mind: "I'll go where you want me to go, dear Lord."

I had a conversation with my mother that was a bright spot during this time. When I told her about my decision to join the church, her response was that I was a grown woman who had been brought up right and that she trusted my judgment. She didn't think I would go wrong in my endeavor to be a disciple of Christ. The confirmation I received about the LDS Church resonated within me, I told her, and I knew I needed to follow the Savior in this way. Sometimes it is hard to understand why God wants us to do one thing or another, I said, but I trusted in the idea that He knows what is best for us, and all I could do was try to faithfully follow Him.

The day of my baptism was a beautiful, sunny day. The missionaries had concerns because they knew I had an earlier commitment to direct the youth choir at my former church that same day, so when we arrived at the LDS chapel one of the missionaries jumped up and down in his excitement, seeing that we had made it in time. This was the beginning of a wonderful journey in the gospel for me.

I prayed from the first day I joined the church that I would see others of my race enter the ward, and I have been blessed to see that happen. It may be difficult for some to grasp my conversion in light of the controversy over priesthood ordination. If blacks could not be full members of the church in times past, why should they join the church now? It was certainly disconcerting to learn that people were denied privileges because of their skin color, something I had to pray about and search the scriptures for. After studying and much consideration, I realized that racism had such a long history I could not unravel everything that had transpired; I had to trust that God would not withhold His blessings indefinitely and that He knows what is best.

After joining the church, I almost immediately received a ward calling as the Relief Society chorister, which helped me learn the hymns I was unfamiliar with. The sisters and brothers in the ward were more than helpful and supportive. Over the years, I have learned so much through the sacrament, Sunday school, and Relief Society meetings and callings I received in Relief

Society education, Gospel Principles, and as one of the choir directors. Things were going so well for us that I could not anticipate the test that soon turned my world around: divorce.

At first I was extremely hurt by the breakup. Since the emphasis in the LDS Church is on families, I wondered how other members would treat me. Even if they didn't treat me poorly, as broken, how would I identify with them now? Would they accept me as a single mom with two young children? My son had been raised in the church since age two and my daughter had been born into the church. Our family had been sealed in the Washington temple a year after my daughter's birth. It was the only church they knew. I thought I would feel out of place now in the presence of intact families. My bishops were helpful, and I had friends at church who offered support, so my fears subsided.

The time it took to heal from the divorce passed slowly. Eventually, I recognized that God loved me no matter what my circumstances were. That being the case, I decided I would not worry about what others thought of me. I came to see the divorce as a test of my faithfulness: the Lord wanted to see where I might place my trust during a difficult time. I became a stronger person because of what happened. I am better prepared, as a result, for whatever other situations or loss may come to me later in life.

Throughout all these stages of conversion, baptism, and active membership in the church, I have retained a great faith in the gospel. I know that my Heavenly Father loves me and wants me to succeed. I have had good home teachers, visiting teachers, friends, and family who have supported me during my times of trial. My children and I have survived, I have grown stronger, and my experiences have led to other blessings, for which I am grateful.

I have an abiding testimony that I am a valued daughter of God. Others may define me in different ways, but it does not matter to my Savior what color I am or what my marital status is. I see myself, first and foremost, as a woman who is a blessed daughter of God.

10 | Vision Revisions

Marcee Monroe

I didn't know I needed glasses until I was fourteen. In fact, until I went to the DMV to sign up for Driver's Education, I had no idea that my eyesight was less than perfect. I'd always been able to read the chalkboard from the back of the class, so failing a basic eye test at the DMV was startling.

"Next," the bored clerk called. I stepped up to the line and peered through binocular-like openings, eager to ace my first eye test. While tidying her desk, the clerk clicked through the slides and mechanically asked the questions she had memorized. I answered the first questions quickly, motivated to demonstrate I had somehow escaped my parents' genetic eyesight deficiencies. Then we hit a snag.

"Which shape is in front of the others?" the clerk asked from the garbage can at the far end of the room. I blinked. Was it a trick question?

"There isn't one," I stated with as much fact as I could muster. Emptying her hole punch, she repeated the question.

"They are all the same," I reported. Surely in her efficiency, she had pulled up the wrong slide.

"You can't see one shape in front of the others?" she asked, bending to pick up the stray hole-punch circles on the floor. My smugness slipping, I looked again and saw clearly three crisp shapes in a row. I had no idea what I was supposed to be seeing.

"You need glasses."

It turns out that while my left eye was strong enough to see distances, my right eye was too weak to pass the depth perception test. Both eyes need to be equally strong to perceive depth, and my left eye could not compensate. This hadn't impaired my ability to function in the world—I had yet to walk into a tree—but now I needed to function at a faster speed. There was also so much I had been missing, like seeing the individual leaves on a tree in gradations of color instead of a mass of green. Without strength in both eyes, not only was I unable to see clearly, I couldn't see deeply. Correcting my vision brought awe, wonder, and depth to my life. In the fourteen-plus years since my vision was corrected, I have learned in ways beyond optometry that the world is breathtaking when you can see it clearly and deeply.

———•———

The view from our usual pew, six rows from the front, was particularly inspiring one Sunday morning. My four-year-old leaned over to kiss my nine-month pregnant belly and tell me how much she already loved her baby brother. I basked in a maternal glow as my two golden-haired girls behaved like the angels they looked like in matching Easter dresses. On my other side sat my best friend, Jill, who had come to visit for the weekend. The first speaker, Christine, was someone I'd admired since I was a teenager, a woman who personified the Young Woman Recognition Award Medallion, the trinket given to girls for certain spiritual, service, and home-oriented achievements. Of course, she was beautiful, slender, had light in her eyes and grace in her step. She also had a sparkling sense of humor and a feistiness that, to me, solidified her image as a strong and virtuous woman—a pattern of living I held in my mind as a model to follow. After she spoke, her six kids performed a musical number that provoked tears from my hormone-riddled body as I imagined my kids singing in the future.

Then her husband stood and offered up words of praise I have heard countless times from men at the pulpit, announcing love and gratitude for his wife and then celebrating how devoted she is. I had often rolled my eyes at such public and self-congratulatory expressions of love. But that day I was caught up in the celebration of motherhood and hardly noticed the word "devoted" until Jill stifled a sneer, catching me off guard by her disdain for the word.

What I had let pass as a harmless cliché, Jill saw as derogatory, as if the husband praising his wife's devotion was like praising her chains. Jill saw Christine not as an agent of her life but as a captive of her role, who was taken advantage of and imposed upon in the name of religious belief. Stripping away the cliché, however, being devoted involves powerful, sanctifying actions. Devotion is "to dedicate by a vow, sacrifice oneself, promise solemnly."[1] It is not an involuntary reflex or an inevitable circumstance but is the result of a conscious, deliberate choice.

In that moment sitting next to Jill, I saw double. I was jolted back to a time when I too would have cringed at the lavish praise being bestowed on a woman for being able to procreate and tend children, back to a time when I saw domesticity as chains. Like Jill, I had once been full of my own share of indignation at what seemed like an expectation in our culture of limits on a woman's options, of offering up women as sacrifices in the name of motherhood and calling it noble.

———•———

I remember the day, as a freshman in college, I came home and voiced to my roommate what felt like a shocking confession, a concern that had been banging around in my head for some time: "Is my contribution to the world

1. *Online Etymology Dictionary*, s.v. "devoted," www.etymonline.com.

to be *only* through bearing children? Is that all?" It felt wrong to utter it, like I was betraying my own mother's decisions. Behind it was the raw angst of a nineteen-year-old whose world had just become bigger. I went from working summers at a snow-cone shack in a farming town of 9,000 to studying at a state university of 15,000 where I was on dual scholarship: one for academics and one for theater performance. When I wasn't working on a show, on or off the stage, I was enthralled with the honors classes that challenged my thinking. I also worked for the opera company teaching children about drama and creativity. I had no firm career plans but was caught up in a thrilling adventure with the world and how I would contribute to it. The potential was electrifying. I wanted to make an impact with my mind and talents.

And yet, since my youth, I had always wanted to be a mother, more than anything else. As a young woman, I frequently had this internal conversation about what I would give up to be a mother. I was willing to sacrifice any dream, goal, or ambition *if* it came down to that. I would do it "in a heartbeat, without delay," I said to myself. I could somehow feel a phantom pain and loss at the possibility of arms empty of children. After a semester of college, though, I felt a pain of loss at the possibility of being *only* a mother, empty of my own dreams. It certainly didn't occur to me that you could do both. My murky feelings seemed at odds with my mother's experience.

Motherhood lit her up. "Every fiber of my being," she would say, radiated the rightness of it. I wanted more and that felt wrong. The contradiction filled my field of vision; I couldn't see past it.

———•———

When I was a sophomore, I voiced to my roommate what felt like another shocking confession. "I think I might be a feminist," I whispered. My roommate nodded knowingly and said, "Me too." It felt dangerous and thrilling. The idea had germinated in a class I was taking in multicultural American literature with Dr. Jennifer Sinor. Growing up, I thought feminism was the F-word thanks to Rush Limbaugh's mocking of what he called *femi-nazis*. In Dr. Sinor's class, though, I not only began to understand the foundational principles of the movement and the power of feminism in understanding culture, I also met a real feminist, the first I had come to know personally.

Professor Sinor was not just beautiful in a hip, thin, "I can pull off straight bangs" kind of way; her small frame carried a quiet, unmistakable power and self-confidence with its own beauty that was reassuring rather than intimidating. She did not seem to be capable of self-doubt or pride, and she had compassion for those unlike herself. Her classes were what my classmates and I called brain burners: they broke down our assumptions about the world and left us with the burning feeling of muscles being pushed to their limit. It was exhilarating.

Wanting more, I delved into Betty Friedan's *Feminine Mystique* on my own time. I found myself shouting in agreement as Friedan explained the plight of women; with seer-like wisdom she read the bones of domesticity in her temple of academia and divined the source of trouble from the cracks in women's souls. I'm probably exaggerating the depth of reverence I gave her ideas, but I was enthusiastic. Friedan wrote about the identity crisis women faced by not confronting the discrepancy between their assigned roles and their personal desires, talents, and potential. To avoid confrontation, women passively retreated into domesticity. I began to see today's women in similar roles, as still experiencing this same personal crisis. There was so much to process, I tried to write my way into understanding. In one essay after another, I wrestled with femininity, sexuality, and my own painfully damaged body image, all through the intellectual framework of feminism. I began the process of unravelling my identity from cultural expectations.

I then tried to work it out with my mother, to lay out these feminist ideas that were so new and tender to me. None of it resonated with her. When she was young, feminism represented an attack on her most sacred beliefs, and here I was identifying with that same group that had ridiculed her choices. Social change is divisive at its birth and in its infancy, with every movement eventually maturing into an older and wiser version of itself. My mom knew feminism when it was still a nasty teenager, the meanest girl in junior high. I met the same girl at her high school reunion and she opened my eyes. Out of the research I did came a determination to discover myself before I decided anything about my future.

After my conversion to feminism, I went about the business of finding myself and forging an identity. I fell in love, took Spanish 101, transferred to BYU, changed my major to English, had my heart broken, cut my hair short and dyed it purple, took Welsh 101, stopped running three miles a day, took up yoga, joined the BYU Honor's Program, fell in love again, protested the war in Iraq, wrote three different honor's proposals, took German 101, supported the war on terror, grew my hair out, took up rock climbing, and broke someone's heart. Through it all, I wrote and kept coming back to what it meant to be a woman in various roles[2] as if the key to my identity could be found if I just studied the world enough with my intellectual eye.

---

2. I wrote essays on Christina Rosetti's narrative poem, *Goblin Market*; Elizabeth Barrett Browning's *Aurora Leigh*; Romantic writers like Felicia Hemans; Victorian etiquette manuals; books on manners from the 1950s and 1970s; and classics from Jane Austen, the Brontë sisters, George Elliot, and Virginia Woolf. I also looked at ethnic writers like Gloria Anzaldúa, Gwendolyn Brooks, Ana Castillo, Toni Morrison, and Helena Maria Viramontes.

For years I struggled with the age-old contradiction most evident, I thought, in the counsel LDS leaders were giving young women to prepare for a career but to be prepared to give it up. On the one hand, my future felt limited by marriage prospects and eventually my body's ability to bear children, both factors out of my control. Yet it also seemed unfair to give my mind, time, heart, and money to something I might never use. My ability to choose had limits, single or married. By the end of college, I had concluded that I needed something more than motherhood, at least a part-time avocation to ground me, so I wouldn't lose myself in the roles I played. I would need something to hold onto outside of motherhood, something to help me keep sight of who I am.

———•———

Just when I had accepted a single life, I met a man better than my dreams. We married after my first grueling semester of grad school and chose to start a family right away. I became pregnant a year later, and instead of working on my master's thesis, I researched pregnancy and childbirth, including the history and science of it and everything in between. I was engrossed by the life emerging in my belly, captivated by the awesome power of my body going through enormous changes, and distracted by the accompanying discomforts. When I had my baby, I no longer wanted to finish my master's thesis. I was too tired.

In the first months after having my baby, I found little in my day-to-day tasks that was amazing or elevated. I was too exhausted and drowning in hormones to feel much of anything but deep relief. Relief when I could soothe my baby, get another few minutes of sleep, or eat some good food. On the whole, I was terrified of motherhood.

I remember sitting on a bench in the entry of my new apartment building, bouncing my baby on my lap as I waited for my ride to some baby appointment. Every part of me still felt swollen, puffy, and drippy. My body was a stranger. I was sleep-deprived. It was like being initiated into an elite sorority with the worst kind of hazing possible. An older woman from down the hall came by and sighed over my newborn.

"How old is she?" the woman asked, beginning the same conversation I'd had with everyone I met.

"Four weeks," I said. *Was it only four weeks?*

"They grow up fast," she said, smiling. I tried to return the smile, to look happy and motherly instead of exhaustedly desperate.

Not fast enough! I thought. *I can't do this much longer.*

"Treasure this time; it'll be gone before you know it," she said as she continued on her way to her apartment. I did smile then, but only ironically. I couldn't see past this hellish cycle of near-constant nursing and nearly absent sleeping. There were so many moments I wanted to run away. I couldn't think straight or see clearly, but I hung on by a mix of instinct and faith. A year into motherhood, I finally started to feel more comfortable than awkward and uncertain. It took a year for me find the energy to finish my master's thesis, something I no longer felt passionate about, I was so consumed with my daughter. Before becoming a mother, my master's work was my lifeline. A year in, it felt like a waste of time. I spent more than four years on women's studies and feminism and came only to tentative conclusions. I spent a year on an intellectual hiatus doing the repetitive tasks of motherhood such as feeding, comforting, and wiping up bodily fluids, and I somehow had a firm testimony of motherhood as ennobling. The change seemed like a miracle, this testimony a gift. I had begun to see things like my mother.

As I write this essay one-handed, another weeks-old baby on my lap, my heart is different. This time it feels hallowed instead of just hard. Contrary to what I fretted about in college, I don't feel like I've lost myself in motherhood. Instead, I feel that my identity has been magnified. Nothing I had ever accomplished or achieved parallels what I have done in seven devoted years as a mother. The depth of my devotion to both motherhood and feminism continues to astonish me.

———•———

For centuries women were considered inferior humans, even as they were told that the act of mothering was "near to divinity."[3] I am grateful for the people who challenged this notion of inferiority. Feminism added to my understanding of what it means to be female apart from fertility. I saw in feminism the values of cooperation and compassion, values shared by my faith, that I felt to be instinctual in women as opposed to the competition and hierarchical structures of the patriarchy.[4] Feminism helped me stop looking at my self-aspirations with an eye of competition, removing the adversarial relationship between motherhood and my personal dreams.

Feminism also gave me a lens to see womanhood more clearly, absent culture's clothes and confines. I am indebted to Friedan because she asked me to confront cultural and personal expectations of myself, to question what it means to be feminine and to ultimately force myself to take responsibility for my identity. But contrary to what I had assumed in college, not every struggling woman living out the traditional role of mother is suffering from Friedan's identity crisis. Sometimes life is

3. Russell M. Nelson, "Our Sacred Duty to Honor Women," *Ensign*, May 1999, online at "magazines," www.lds.org.

4. I use "patriarchy" here as a feminist term, with no biblical or religious associations. In feminism, the term patriarchy is a redefinition and extension of the original word to describe the totality of oppression and exploitation of women. It does not refer to acts of domination of individual men but to the system of social structures that perpetuate the power imbalance between the sexes.

exhausting and identity is something built over time. While Friedan did not provide a Plan of Happiness for smothered, unfulfilled women, she added depth of vision for me so I could extricate myself from culture and watch as the seeming contradictions gradually resolved into a clearer picture of womanhood.

Arriving at this place of peace in my current role has been my own personal journey. My path included intellectual questioning and the practical work and experience of motherhood. Both were essential but still insufficient. I don't think peace came to me simply because I had read enough, written enough, changed enough diapers, birthed enough babies, or even said enough prayers or exercised enough faith. Ultimately, the peace I feel is a gift from God. Through grace, my weak eyes have gained strength. As the pace of my life has picked up and demanded better vision, God has granted the perspective I need. I've begun to see deeply not because of the intellectual or maternal journey but because God gave me glasses.

If I could go back and counsel the girl I was as a freshman, I would not attempt to answer whether her contribution to the world would only be through her children. I would tell her that her questions are vital, that there is nothing "only" about her. I would tell her that developing her potential is something she owes to herself and to God, not to the world or a future family, and that there are no limits on her womanhood. I would challenge her to embrace the seeming contradictions, to jump into the world and learn all she could while staying devoted to God and true to herself. I would promise her that if she did, her vision would improve. She would see more beauty, distinction, and depth in her womanhood. And it would take her breath away.

11 | Wounded
Rachel Brown

The American novelist and religious writer Sue Monk Kidd asserted in her autobiography, *Dance of the Dissident Daughter*, that there is a feminine wound in religion: an unconscious but pervasive internalization of the idea that to be female is to be inferior.[1] I felt the pain of that wound before I could articulate what I was experiencing. I've heard women speak of their "feminist awakening," when they realized disparities they had not previously considered, but I don't remember waking up. I just remember pain.

I grew up in the warm nest of a multi-generational Mormon family, nourished with poetry and epic family tales of spiritual heroism. The LDS Church was the center of all our lives, and to be good was to be true to the gospel. I admired the profound faith and goodness of my elders and wanted to be righteous like them. I was endlessly loved, but I was also Goddess-starved and taught that I was not my own person.

---

1. Kidd, *The Dance of the Dissident Daughter: A Woman's Journey from Christian Tradition to the Sacred Feminine* (San Francisco: HarperCollins, 1996), 28.

At a very young age, I understood that girls were for home and boys were for anything. I used to squirm during Young Women's lessons as week after week we were taught to support the priesthood and see our place as eternal followers, not leaders. Men were the doers in God's kingdom, women the bearers of men's souls.

During these lessons, I imagined myself as a pretty doll that one day would be chosen and taken to the temple to be married. I was to cover up my body until a man selected me, bought me with a diamond ring, and took me home to unwrap. Heavenly Mother was a pretty doll too, tucked away safely on the shelf in some glorious kingdom, kept out of sight so no one would break Her. I learned that my worth depended on whether or not a man found me attractive, deigned to allow me to support him in his trajectory through life, put me in his pocket when he strode off to grad school, and made me a mother. The narrative I was given about earth and heaven taught me that to be female was to be a creature to be acted upon, while to be male was to act.

I remember wishing I could find myself as a protagonist in the scripture stories I loved. As a reader, I connected easily with the scriptural narrative. I was comforted, strengthened, and inspired by my scripture study. However, my experiences were bittersweet; the frequent misogynist passages hurt me. Despite wanting to feel uplifted, the scriptures reaffirmed that women were less important than men in the grand scheme of things. In fact, it seemed that women were despised for not being men. Under the Law of Moses, for instance, a woman's postpartum period of *uncleanness* was twice as long if she gave birth to a girl rather than a boy. Peter referred to wives as weaker vessels,[2] and countless scriptural stories portray women as existing for men's pleasure or progress rather than as entities unto themselves. Paul's remarks about women submitting to their husbands and keeping silent in church magnified my fears. My seminary teacher joked that "Paul had the right idea!"

I lamented the lack of female voices especially in the Book of Mormon. I wrote in high school, "Why didn't they consider the possible merits of having some female heroes among these voices from the dust? Maybe no one else would care, but it would mean so much to me. And the very fact that they didn't consider it must mean we're insignificant. I love the story of the stripling warriors, but it's given to [my brothers] and not to me. What stories of ourselves ARE given to girls? What can I wish for?"

When I looked to the heavens, I could not see my own face—or a Mother's face who looked like mine. I felt a pang when I read, "male and female created He them" (Gen. 1:27)—the Almighty "She" missing. I wanted to

2. 1 Pet. 3:7.

read about a woman, hear about a woman who had a body like mine, learn about her dealings with God and her spiritual progression. We did not speak about or pray to our Mother in Heaven, I was told, because God respected Her so much He would not allow His children to vilify Her name. This Victorian-age explanation satisfied my peers, but to me it was a stinging indication of what I could expect out of a celestial lifestyle. I would be "locked away in a basement knitting" if I went to heaven, I wrote furiously in my journal. It seemed duplicitous to teach young girls that their greatest aspiration should be motherhood and then have the ultimate mother missing in action, reduced to a theological assumption and two lines in a hymn by Eliza R. Snow. Even as exalted women in the next life, presumably we would be invisible, silent ciphers, non-entities in a process of populating cosmic colonies.

An unhelpful suggestion was that perhaps we didn't learn about our Mother in church because there were myriad Heavenly Mothers who were God's plural wives. Becoming aware of the church's history of plural marriage amplified my anguish. It was devastating to find out that polygamy was part of the church's past. I felt betrayed—not just that it happened historically but that it was expected to exist in heaven and that men were still sealed to more than one woman in the temple.

I stayed up late arguing with my mother about the topic. The prayer for understanding I had been instructed to offer to God came out like a muffled scream: "How could you?" As a teenager I read in section 132 of the Doctrine and Covenants that God told Emma Smith if she didn't accept other women "given" to her husband, she would be destroyed. How could this be the same loving incarnation of God who gathered the little children into His arms? How could I trust this Father, whose love seemed to shine over His sons but who seemed to cast His daughters into the shadows?

For years I could barely speak about the damage that polygamy did to my relationship with God without weeping. I spent hours in the black holes of my soul. I could not see how a loving Father could force His daughters into marriages that left so many of them lonely and unfulfilled.

My feminist angst in those years was amplified by isolation. No one else in my spiritual community seemed afflicted by the same struggles. My cumulative questions about women broke out occasionally like hives in a series of neuroses. When I took my questions to leaders, relatives, friends, and roommates, seeking a cure, everyone seemed to have a handy dismissive explanation for my malady. I had uncles who were willing to lecture me about why my place in the eternal plan was one of honor (I was listening to "the world" and didn't properly understand), roommates who bore their testimonies of the privilege of motherhood, women at church who plied me with platitudes about girls being born good and virtuous so they don't need the priesthood, whereas boys need it to keep them from raping and pillaging. When such banalities failed to heal me, there was always the verbal shutdown, someone advising me to "put it on the shelf for now," that "God's ways are not our ways." I was told I should spend my time on something more "pertinent to my salvation."

Despite the continued pain, I sincerely believed in the gospel. I could not disconnect from the church and its issues and simply blow them off. For me it was the only reality that existed. I have since met people whose Mormonism is porous, who are able to shift and sift. Mine was more like a choke hold: I felt I had no other choice than to believe it all. At the same time, I was developing an interest in volunteer work and service and felt I was becoming closer to the Savior. Parts of my testimony grew strong and healthy during that period, while others twisted and stunted. The mental gymnastics I engaged in to reconcile my doubts and beliefs were exhausting. I believed every word in every antiquated lesson manual and every word spoken over the pulpit. I had been trained to believe that doubt was a deception from the adversary. Feeling mental agony at church was just a sign of spiritual weakness.

For years, I dreamed of serving a full-time mission. It was such a revered part of my family's culture that I wanted my own chance to go out in the world and declare glad tidings. However, whenever I expressed my desire to serve outside of my family, I was rebuked. My seminary teachers teased me, "Girls who look like you don't serve missions." Young Women leaders cautioned me that although women were allowed to serve, my first priority as a girl was to find a husband and begin a family. I was told that I should only consider a mission if I failed to find a husband after making an honest effort. I began to recoil whenever I heard the clause, "When you young men go on missions, and when you young women get married ... " I used to think, No, no, no, I will have my own moments of light and times of darkness, my own humbling mission stories and slang. My own mission call. My own adventure. My own coming-of-age experiences on the mountain with God. I also recognized that returned missionaries commanded reverence and respect in the church context. I knew that people would listen to me more, that my insights would carry more weight if I could reference missionary work and experiences.

The discouragement I received troubled me so much that I appealed to authority. When I was seventeen, I wrote a letter to the church president about my concern as a female not having been "invited to the party" in terms of mission service. I cited Doctrine and Covenants section 4, that whoever had desires to serve was called to the work. I suggested that girls should not be advised against going; surely missionary preparation and service would only benefit them and their future families. I thought the response would be "We would love to have you!" but instead, a secretary returned my letter with quotations from a President Hinckley sermon,[3] with this statement: "Serving a mission should never interfere with a proposal of marriage. ... If the desire [to serve] persists, talk to your bishop, and he will know what to do." I found this humiliating. Not only was my suggestion rejected, my desire was treated like a persistent cough.

I was frustrated that I was only being offered one path for my life without being allowed to decide for myself. I continued to struggle with church talks extolling the virtues of womanhood and the divine role of women, which gave me feelings of repulsion I didn't understand at the time. Those acquainted with my issues, so to speak, referred me to the same sermons that were causing me such anguish; these well-intentioned people were always confused when their counsel didn't satisfy me.

Gloria Steinem's words resonated with me during this time: "A pedestal is as much a prison as any small, confined space."[4] Confined is what I felt. The God I believed

---

3. Hinckley, "Some Thoughts on Temples, Retention of Converts, and Missionary Service," *Ensign,* Nov. 1997, online at lds.org/general-conference/1997/.

4. Qtd. in Gina Salamone, "The Gloria Steinem Factor: On Feminist Icon's Seventy-fifth Birthday," *Daily News*, Mar. 24, 2009, online at www.nydailynews.com.

in had wept with Enoch with a heart that "swelled wide as eternity."[5] I didn't understand why such an expansive God would require such a proscribed life for me.

I was told throughout my life that I would feel closest to God in the temple, so I felt particularly betrayed to see the subordination of women explicitly dramatized there. I had hoped, shyly, for beauty, insight, and warmth from heaven—Christ's hand "stretched out still"[6]—and I entered the sacred doors with the highest hopes. Instead, I felt that my fears of being "less than" in the eternal sense were confirmed, and this was devastating. Each time I attended, I felt a terrible sense of loneliness among people who seemed to be basking in peace while I was suffering. Attending the temple when required was excruciating for me and traumatic for my companions because they were so bewildered by my pain. The platitudes swept through again, seeking to heal but just adding to the pain: "God would never ask you to do something that wasn't good for you ... Sometimes we need to be more humble ... You don't have to obey your husband unless he's being obedient to God!" None of that was enough for me.

In the middle of this mental torture, I began to define myself as a feminist, and not in a positive way at first. I was aware that feminists were thought to be in conflict

5. Moses 7:41.
6. Moses 7:30.

with the church, angry, and bitter, and that was how I felt. When I raised issues with roommates or guys I dated, they were quick to ask, "You're not a feminist, are you?" A member of the branch presidency at the Mission Training Center reprimanded me when I suggested that elders didn't need to stand up every time I entered a room. "Welcome to the church. This is how we do things," he said. "Do you want to be here or not?" When I found myself so shocked and upset that I was unable to respond, he told me to smile.

In my private writings, I referred to the violent dissonance I experienced as my "feminist rages." They were my ugliest flaw, my deepest weakness. People close to me suggested that this was my personal trial, but I didn't understand why I would be given a trial that made God's good and kind plan seem abhorrent to me. Emotionally, I felt I was holding my hands directly over a flame. Although my flesh was searing, I couldn't pull my hands away.

This was the nature of my feminine wound: inexplicable pain when I was supposed to feel peace and joy. After living in the information age for a few years, I found it astonishing to think of how disconnected I was. I was stunningly alone, with no blogs, no forums, no Facebook posts to hint that there were others who felt as I did.

My issues with gender roles made dating difficult and somewhat paradoxical. I fell in love and wanted to be close, but I was always conscious of power differentials and felt something close to disgust that I'd lose some of my freedom. I often told myself that the only way I could be equal would be to remain single and autonomous, with no husband to preside over me. I was loath to even discuss marriage.

Jonathan was different. Although at first he was confused about my angst over gender roles, he listened and opened his mind. He was one of the first people to ever validate my pain, to reach for me with empathy rather than to shame me for my lack of faith. He was a critical thinker, and I trusted him—first with my thoughts, later with my heart and life. I believe I was drawn to my partner because something in me recognized how much he would eventually understand and how we would be able to leave the pain behind together. We made one another safe in a way neither of us had experienced before, and that safety helped create a space for spiritual exploration.

Birth

Becoming a mother was so connected to the archetypes of submission and oppression for me that I needed a way to give birth that allowed me to claim the event for myself. With my first child, I chose to birth at home with a midwife. I was unprepared for the backlash that erupted from my family. I understand that there was genuine concern for my safety; nevertheless, at the time, choosing to give birth in a way that also fulfilled my needs was liberating. I felt that the roof of my life had been torn away and all that reigned above me was sheer, endless sky. I insisted that this was mine: My life, my body, my soul!

The conversations I had about birth mirrored my discussions about the role of women in the church. Although I have now moved into a place of respect for the unpredictability of birth, and I know that each birth is its own intimate world, I benefited from learning about the paternalistic nature of medically managed births in the Western world. I developed an appreciation for the bodily autonomy of birthing women and the importance of allowing their voices to be heard. "Who are you to question a doctor?" sounded exactly like "Who are you to question the Brethren?" I began to ask my questions with dignity rather than self-loathing.

These churning clouds of shifting thoughts dissipated the day I gave birth to my son. I started out giggling and silly at the beginning, then slipped into a deeper intensity as my body became absorbed by the relentless process of birth. Being in my own body during labor was humbling. There was no way out but through the pain. It was intense, but I felt cradled and supported. Jonathan leaned his forehead against mine and held me. He told me I was a warrior, that I was birthing beautifully. My friends, my doulas, wrapped their arms around me, pressed down on my back and shoulders, stroked my hair and forehead, and whispered that I could do this—it was mine. The doulas carried me through it, the beauty and pain of the shared experience the most potent sisterhood I've ever felt.

It was so unexpected—the heartbreak of it, the glory I found within my body. When I was pushing, bringing my baby down, I reached within my soul and found I was a being capable of colossal strength. Holding my floppy, flailing, fish-like child against my neck, feeling his sweet movements and hearing him squeak, I cried and kissed him all over his vernixy head. I rose triumphant from that birth pool with my son in my arms.

That day I learned that I was not inferior. I was a bright and strong being after all. Whatever God was, whether it was "two men and a bird"[7] or an ancient Mother goddess who stood beside me that day like a doula, Her hand on my shoulder, Her face peering into my blind face, I don't know, but I felt God with me that day. I felt my own heart stretch "wide as eternity." It was the day I began to love myself.

Taking this new life in my hands was when I symbolically took my own life into my hands. I now find myself in every story and any story, and I am free to take from these stories what nourishes me and discard what does not. Frail justifications for sexism and lack of inclusion

---

[7]. Sandra M. Schneiders, "God Is More Than Two Men and a Bird," *U.S. Catholic*, May 1990, p. 20; paraphrased in an interview with Sue Monk Kidd at the author's website, suemonkkidd.com.

cannot bind me any longer. I am the author of my own life, and the canon is open.

I do not blame myself for feeling wounded by doctrines that were genuinely bringing me pain. I now see my "feminist rages" as my natural response to messages that were legitimately problematic and distressing. I no longer feel any need to repent or apologize for that pain. I honor my past self who struggled so hard, served a mission despite opposition, and endured loneliness until she found someone who acknowledged her pain and helped seek the source of it rather than blame her for the symptoms. With a new perspective, I was finally able to listen to what my pain was trying to tell me.

I still have a scar from my feminine wound, but I no longer feel wounded. I feel I've grown bigger and beyond what hurt me. There is now space in my life for mystery and the unknown. The kingdom of God is within me, and I am healed.

12 | Divine Nature
Camille Strate Fairbanks

After living in Canada for six years, I've had my fair share of slips and falls on slick surfaces. At ice rinks or on winter sidewalks, it's always the same: one moment I'm standing confidently and the next moment I'm catapulting through space, eyes frantic, arms flapping in search of anything to soften or even slow my fall. No matter where I am or how I fall, my first thought is always the same: *Please don't let this hurt me.*

Please don't let this hurt me: the simplest form of self-preservation, a plea to gravity, which neither knows nor cares about us. It's a futile prayer, but anyone who has fallen knows how equally futile it is to quell such a plea. It's like a flinch. It's in our nature to see impending pain and hope it doesn't hurt us.

And that moment—that drawn-out suspension between vertical and horizontal, that space of time lasting only seconds but feeling like an hour—that is how I felt the moment I learned I was pregnant: *Please don't let this hurt me.*

Then came the guilt.

I battled armies of guilt for weeks after my initial reflex. Why was my first instinct to feel concern for myself rather than my baby? Hadn't I been taught that mothers must be selfless? Why wasn't I thrilled to be having a baby? I should be thrilled. Where was the joy? I should be anticipating my baby with excitement; every child should be welcomed into the world with exhilaration. I felt I had already failed as a mother the moment I became one.

As weeks passed, I couldn't shake my twin demons: both the lack of excitement and guilt over not feeling excited. I was trapped in a vicious cycle, and when I say cycle I should probably say cyclone. Stuck in its vortex, I mourned my former life and regretted that I was mourning when presumably so many women would be thrilled to be in my situation.

It was a very unhealthy time for me.

I didn't admit these feelings to anyone because of how ashamed I felt for having them. Even my husband did not understand my torment. He could tell I was anxious, but I couldn't admit, even to him, that the bulk of my stress came from my lack of joy about motherhood. I was afraid that expressing anything less than glee would be interpreted as not loving the baby.

———•———

When I was a teenager, I babysat a lot. I babysat so much that I got a tremendous glimpse into the many unpleasant realities of motherhood: the wails of colicky infant cousins determined to be unhappy; arguing siblings; sticky, crumb-coated kitchen floors; the stench of sour milk; chaotic bedtimes; sinks piled high with dishes; bottles with tiny plastic pieces that somehow always disappeared at the exact moment the baby was screaming to be fed. And the demands of those children—relentless! "I want to play video games. I want to read a book. I'm hungry. I'm thirsty. I'm cold. I can't find my shoe. I can't find my *other* shoe. I *am* allowed to jump on the couch. I have to go potty. My mom always lets us eat candy for dinner."

The older I grew and the more I babysat, the more cynical I became about children in general. I hated the stickiness. I hated being pulled in as many directions as there were children. I hated being hungry and having to forage for food in an unfamiliar pantry, hated feeling like I needed to remove evidence of having done so despite invitations to "eat anything you'd like" (which couldn't possibly mean the *truly* good stuff like pouches of fruit snacks or cans of soda).

More than anything else, I hated that at the end of every babysitting stint I felt obligated to smile and cheerfully report, "They were great! No problems at all," no matter how rough it had been. There seemed to be some sort of unwritten law—a babysitter's code or maybe just a female stereotype—forbidding any disparaging words against anything domestic, especially to the parents of unruly children.

What I hated most about babysitting was that I had to pretend to like it.

———•———

This hatred of pretense is at the root of my persistent anxiety about motherhood. What if I don't like it? I'll have to pretend. Women who don't like motherhood—whether they are already mothers or simply aren't interested in becoming mothers—are, by our culture's definition, Bad Women.

Of course, we don't usually hear the words "You're a bad woman." At least not directly. That would be rude, and rude women are Bad Women too. We are masters of passive-aggressive behavior, so the words are implied at the park, on Facebook, and sadly, at church. That kind of subtle shaming makes a lot of people, including me, feel compelled to pretend.

Unlike babysitting, where the pretense of cheerfulness has a guaranteed time limit, the pretense of enjoying motherhood could last for, well, eternity. If I didn't like babysitting, at least I knew it would be over in an evening. If it turns out that I don't like motherhood ... there's really no going back. I will either have to pretend to be thrilled about having children or be a Bad Mother—and by extension, a Bad Woman.

The longer I considered my difficult position, the greater my angst grew, and my instinct toward self-preservation again prompted me to flail my arms and pray, "Please don't let this hurt me." Only this time it felt hopeless because there were so many ways I knew it would.

———•———

I used to bristle during my Young Women classes when the teacher talked about the "divine nature" of women. It was one of the eight core Young Women values: "faith, divine nature, individual worth, knowledge, choice and accountability, good works, integrity, and virtue." I understood this particular value to be the "wife and mother" value. Lessons on divine nature used womanhood as the passageway to wifedom and motherhood. Where I craved to be told that just being a woman, a daughter of God, was enough to merit heavenly approbation, instead I was taught that, in fact, it was not. Because I was a woman, I was therefore destined, even foreordained, to grow up, get married, and have babies. Moreover, I should be sweet and cheerful about such a future because, again as a woman, it was my calling in life. It was what God wanted, according to the lessons on divine nature, and that was that.

Even more frustrating to me, however, was that this interpretation of my wife-and-mother destiny seemed based more on Mormon culture than actual doctrine.

The divine nature–themed scriptures referenced in the Young Women's *Personal Progress* handbook are not wife- and mother-focused. For example, Doctrine and Covenants 121:45 reads,

> Let thy bowels also be full of charity towards all men, and to the household of faith, and let virtue garnish thy thoughts unceasingly; then shall thy confidence wax strong in the presence of God; and the doctrine of the priesthood shall distil upon thy soul as the dews from heaven.

Charity toward all, unceasing virtue, and faith in God are all good traits, but the scripture does not mention motherhood. Another passage quoted in the handbook is Proverbs 31:10–31, a section about the qualities of a "virtuous woman" that has nothing to do with tending babies. The woman in Proverbs possesses talents in the business world: she "considereth a field, and buyeth it: with the fruit of her hands she planteth a vineyard." She produces merchandise, fashions clothing for sale, and helps the poor. Nowhere does it say she operates a nursery. In fact, the implication is that she has employees for that: "She ... giveth meat to her household, and a portion to her maidens."

Lastly, Alma 7:23–24 reads,

> And now I would that ye should be humble, and be submissive and gentle; easy to be entreated; full of patience and long-suffering; being temperate in all things;

being diligent in keeping the commandments of God at all times; asking for whatsoever things ye stand in need, both spiritual and temporal; always returning thanks unto God for whatsoever things ye do receive. And see that ye have faith, hope, and charity, and then ye will always abound in good works.

Surprisingly, this passage is not addressed to women at all but to "my beloved brethren" (v. 22). Still, the passage suggests traits we can all embrace. Ultimately, there is nothing in the scriptures telling women, "And now I would that ye should grow up, get married young, have lots of babies, and stay at home making bread all the days of thy life." You could if you chose to, of course, but it's not a commandment.

"The Family: A Proclamation to the World" is also cited in the *Personal Progress* handbook. Although it is an official statement issued by church leaders, it hasn't actually been canonized as doctrine. Reading it, I can see how women could interpret it as commanding them to marry and be a stay-at-home mother. I was surprised to learn that none of the female leadership in the church knew it was being written at the time it was composed or had any input on it. Chieko Okazaki, the inspired first counselor in the Relief Society presidency from 1990 to 1997, related in an interview that she felt baffled when she was told the proclamation would be presented at a Relief Society meeting in 1995. "How come we weren't consulted?"

she asked, because if given the chance, the female leadership of the church "could have made a few changes" to improve the document.[1] I wish I knew what changes she would have made.

These are the main scriptures and statements referenced in the divine nature section of the *Personal Progress* handbook—the section that somehow came to be interpreted, at least in the Sunday lessons I attended, to mean that any attitude toward marriage and motherhood other than utmost excitement was somehow wrong. Most of my greatest (though admittedly vague) teenage ambitions seemed at odds with my religion's goals for me. I wanted to attend a prestigious Ivy League university, move to New York City, and work as a top-level executive who wore tailored power suits and vacationed in the Hamptons. I didn't realize it at the time, but it is clear to me now that if the doctrine of the church wasn't explicitly telling me to get married at nineteen and have babies by twenty, it was the clear message being conveyed by the *culture* of the church. What a comfort that realization would have been to my anxious teenage self ten years ago. Instead, I lived for years with the assumption that my own rebellious nature was the problem. I wish

---

1. Chieko N. Okazaki, interviewed by Gregory A. Prince, Nov. 15, 2005, published as "'There Is Always a Struggle': An Interview with Chieko N. Okazaki," *Dialogue: A Journal of Mormon Thought* 45, no. 1 (Spring 2012): 112–40; online at "Archive," www.dialoguejournal.com.

someone had told me that there *was* no problem, and that it was okay if I didn't like children very much. I didn't have to squeeze myself into the mold presented to me.

The lessons on divine nature increased my guilt for not wanting to fulfill this supposedly natural, God-given calling. My reaction to that guilt was to rebel, and my discouraging, years-long babysitting career fueled my anger. The final straw for me came the day I had a particularly bad case of the winter flu. My mother, holding back my hair as I dry heaved into a bile-filled toilet, announced, "This is what pregnancy will be like." I grimaced and heaved violently again. Combined, my teenage experiences created a strong enough sense of antagonism toward motherhood to make my fifteen-year-old self swear off having children. Forever.

———•———

At first, proclaiming I would never have kids was a bit of a teenage joke that allowed me to stand out from the crowd of my more traditional Mormon cohorts. As time went on, however, my Never Having Kids mantra became more than just a passing byline: it was my identity. I scared off more than one suitor in college by casually mentioning my vow. Since I was religious, the majority of guys I dated were sourced from my LDS Institute of Religion classes or from the institute foyer, the singles ward, or blind dates arranged by well-meaning

Mormon friends. In other words, I mainly dated Mormons who were a few years older than me and mostly looking to get married.

In Mormon culture, that "getting married" bit included the assumption that we would more or less immediately begin reproducing, which I had sworn I would not do. Problematic? Not for me. I found it weeded out the uptight dates. Still, even at the height of my rebellion, I knew I wasn't being wholly honest with myself. It wasn't that I "always knew I was meant to be a mother," as friends in high school declared tearfully; I just felt my life would be a little sad without kids. Reason enough to reproduce? Probably not. But it was the only reason I had, tucked quietly in the back of my mind, that kept me from committing 100 percent against having children.

When the time came that I fell in love with the man I would eventually marry, and when he asked how many kids I wanted to have, I answered the question honestly for the first time in my adult life: "I don't know. Maybe three or four?"

It was a breakthrough for me. I admitted that I actually was interested in someday becoming a mother despite years of swearing to the opposite. My journey to motherhood was far from over, however. I still had a drama-filled engagement to mediate, a drawn-out university degree to earn, and hours-long conversations on the matter to work through with my husband. He was ready to have children the year we got married, and I needed five more to come to terms with it.

Fast-forward those five years, and here I am, pregnant and terrified. I don't have a pregnancy glow. I don't have thick, luscious hair. My baby bump is not cute, and I certainly don't own any trendy maternity clothes. By Hollywood's standards, I'm a failure. By the church's cultural standards, I failed long ago. The only standards left are my own, and I am determined to live up to those at least.

———•———

What do I think will make me a good mother?

Patience. Trying to go the majority of days without screaming at my child. Setting an example of health and fitness but also enjoying a good splurge. Knowing how to bandage minor scrapes and knowing when to go to the hospital. Not passing out from the sight of blood on the way there.

Forgiveness. Remembering that I am the mother and my child is the child and that when he says he hates me he probably doesn't mean it, and if he does I can still love him.

Avoiding manipulation. Avoiding guilt trips. Hoping that my son will make the right decisions but knowing that if he doesn't, I will love him anyway.

Firmness mixed with tenderness to create my own

personal blend of nurturing that is neither divine nor foreordained but just how I roll.

Lack of pressure, both on myself as a parent and on my child. Lack of pressure on my husband, too—we're all in this together.

A commenter on my blog once told me, "There is no right or wrong way. There is only your way and their way." I've never met that reader, but her words influenced me as if they had come from a lifelong mentor. They echo through my head whenever I consider my personal relationship with guilt (which, let's face it, is often) because she nailed it: there is no right way. There is no right way to be a wife, mother, or woman. There is only the way we are doing it, each individually, the best we can. It's probably better to not do drugs or abuse our children, but that's not what I'm talking about. I'm talking about cultural expectations.

Since cultures vary, and people within them vary even more, we have to be free to choose the way that makes sense for us. There is no one right choice between giving birth with or without medication, for instance, or choosing breast milk over formula; using cloth or disposable diapers; choosing public schools or private schools or homeschooling; being a stay-at-home mom or a career mom or a somewhere-in-between mom or not a mom at all. There is not a right number of children to have, which includes the possibility of having zero.

In my case, there is no right amount of joy to experience during this pregnancy and no right amount of domestic bliss I have to exude. All this pesky social guilt is an incredible waste of energy. The sooner we purge ourselves of unnecessary guilt, the sooner we can find and make peace with our own inherent greatness—our *true* divine nature.

———•———

Three months into this pregnancy, I was making my way through an iced-over parking lot—common in southern Alberta—when I lost my footing and slipped where it was particularly slick. This time, as I began my descent toward the asphalt, arms flailing in front of me to catch my fall, I remember thinking, as if in slow motion: *Please don't let this hurt my baby.*

Later, I wondered if that moment of concern had transformed me into the selfless mother I "ought to be," thinking only of my child and never about myself. I decided it did not. Suppose I deliver this baby in five months and bring him home and discover that motherhood is as stressful and unfulfilling as I worry it will be—will I have failed? No. Will I be "doing it wrong" if I don't find my life's greatest joy and satisfaction in my child? No. If, contrary to what my years of babysitting taught me, I choose not to maintain any sort of pretense about my upcoming lifestyle changes, will I be a Bad Woman?

No.

What if, instead of judging women as good or bad for any number of perceived successes or failings, we released them from judgment? What if we allowed young women to imagine themselves in all sorts of possibilities without dictating what they should do with their lives? What if my son grew up respecting and supporting their decisions? What if we resisted the cultural temptation to create stifling cookie-cutter forms in favor of a multitude of different shapes? What if we let children develop organically to determine for themselves what their true God-given natures are?

That would be divine indeed.

About the Authors

Carli Anderson is currently working on her PhD in Religious Studies at Arizona State University. She has a BA in Near Eastern Studies and an MA from BYU in Biblical Hebrew and Ancient Near Eastern Religions. She taught Hebrew at BYU for several years and has co-authored works on the Dead Sea Scrolls. She also studied and traveled extensively in Israel and elsewhere. She enjoys hiking, snowshoeing, and anything chocolate.

Rachael Decker Bailey received a BA in English and business management and an MA in English from BYU. She has published essays on Henry James, the women of Shakespeare, and literary theory and teaches writing at Purdue University, where her husband, Neil, is finishing his doctorate in engineering; they are the parents of five children. She blogs at *My Foreign Sky* (theirchronicles.blogspot.com) about her life as a mother, organic gardener, aspiring vegetarian chef, and marathon runner. She is equally passionate about imported cheese and homemade artisan breads (hence the marathons).

Erika Ball graduated with a BS in mathematics and MS in statistics at BYU and has since worked in academia and industry, teaching at Indiana University and participating in the business analytics group at PricewaterhouseCoopers. She recently returned to BYU to teach and work on statistical methods that predict curves over time, one application involving an analysis of light emissions from exploding supernovae. She is about to begin a PhD program at Duke University. She likes to cook, enjoys Zumba, and plays the piano and organ.

Rachel Brown (BSW and MSW degrees) is a certified social worker and clinical therapist at the Family Support and Treatment Center in Utah Valley. She enjoys leading support groups and healing circles, playing with her three children, having late-night existential conversations with her partner, and writing angst-filled memoirs. She served an LDS mission in Houston, Texas.

Karen Challis Critchfield is an avid home chef who is frequently found either in the kitchen or devouring a new cookbook, treating it like a real page-turner. She reads the regular kind of books, too, and loves hiking, video games, singing, and a good game of Ultimate Frisbee.

She has made a hobby of rediscovering herself, so she often tries new things. She is married to her best friend, has two children, and currently resides in Utah.

Camille Fairbanks never figured out what she wanted to do in life but liked English classes well enough to complete a BA in English at the University of Lethbridge. She was then hired as the marketing manager for an automotive dealership, which was about as random a career choice as it sounds. She was born in Mesa, Arizona. She moved to Canada in 2007, where she and her husband remain. At the time of this book's release, the son she writes about in her essay is two years old. Her online site, *Archives of Our Lives* (archiveslives.com), allows her to write about work, marriage, and life as a recovering diet Dr. Pepper addict.

Ashley Mae Hoiland received a BFA in studio arts and an MFA in creative writing, both from Brigham Young University. She has since written and illustrated several children's books, founded a project to get local poetry onto Utah billboards, and started the We Brave Women campaign to publicize women of courage. She lives in Palo Alto with her husband and two small children; her husband is pursuing a doctorate in geology at Stanford. She has a website, *Ashmae* (www.ashmae.com), where her artwork is displayed.

Sylvia Lankford loves music and cannot imagine her life without it. She has studied both piano and voice. She enjoys singing with a number of choirs, including the Mormon Choir of Washington, DC. She believes music is a great medium for spreading the gospel message she loves. She earned a business degree and presently works as a government information specialist handling Freedom of Information requests. She has been a member of the LDS Church for twenty-eight years and is the current Relief Society president in her ward.

Marcee Monroe always loved stories and words, which fueled her pursuit of a BA in creative writing at BYU and an MA from the University of Texas at Austin in rhetoric and composition. She has developed a brand of word art that she and her sister market through their online business, *Jabberdashery* (www.etsy.com/shop/Jabberdashery). She has taught art, music, and theater to children, writing to college students, and the gospel to all ages. Now she homeschools her four enthusiastic, clever, and kind children until she and her husband can open their own school.

Brooke Stoneman is a librarian, book artist, bookbinder, and all-around bibliophile. She graduated from BYU in English and from San Jose State University with an MLIS (Master of Library and Information Science). For her master's degree, she studied illuminated manuscripts and the history of books. She has worked in libraries around the world, including the Middle East, where she and her husband currently live. Her travel essays and book art can be found at her website (www.theworldthatwelivein. com/). She has recently started playing bass guitar.

Colleen Whitley retired in 2006 after twenty years of teaching English and Honors classes at Brigham Young University and serving as advisor for *Insight*, the journal of the Honors Program. She is the author of five books, and she is on the Board of Editors of the *Utah Historical Quarterly*. Her master's thesis involved composing new monologues for Arthurian characters in eight styles of poetry, later published in *BYU Studies*. Over the course of her career, she taught kindergarten through graduate school and classes in special programs such as Job Corps and adult education. She enjoys needlework, hiking in the Wasatch Range, and what she calls "harassing inept public officials."

Jamie Zvirzdin served an LDS Spanish-speaking mission in Toronto before finishing her BA in English and editing from BYU. After six years of working as a science editor for Atomium Culture, a non-profit organization known for publishing science news in Europe, she received an MFA in writing and literature from Bennington College in Vermont. Besides working on her first novel and editing physics and computer-programming textbooks for

Taylor & Francis, she plays racquetball, reads astronomy books with her son, and enjoys being married to a US Foreign Service officer. Over the next few years, she and her family will be in Nicaragua and she will communicate with readers through her personal website (www.jamiezvirzdin.com/) and social media (twitter.com/jamiezvirzdin).

Fresh Courage Take was composed in Requiem, a typeface produced in 1992 by American designer Jonathan Hoefler and modeled after a Renaissance manual by Ludovico Vicentino degli Arrighi. Requiem's italic characters resemble the calligraphy Arrighi produced for the Apostolic Chancery (scribal archives) in Rome.

For the titles, subheads, running head, and page numbers, the modern font Museo was employed, created by Dutch designer Jos Buivenga and based on a daydream Buivenga had in which he bent the ends of the capital U to form tiny serifs. Both typefaces represent a contemporary approach to traditional forms and echo the sensitivity and assertiveness of the personal essays in this volume.

Printed and bound by Sheridan Books in Ann Arbor, Michigan, this book is available to wholesalers through Chicago Distribution Center, a division of the University of Chicago Press that represents some 105 publishers.